Review,
Practice,
& Mastery of **NEW JERSEY**

READING

CORE CURRICULUM
CONTENT STANDARDS

Reviewers

Shauna Easteadt • Shongum School • Randolph, NJ
Marcie Fiorentino • Mount Arlington Public Schools • Mount Arlington, NJ
Elizabeth D. Holley, Ed.D. • Willard School • Ridgewood, NJ
Matthew Keller • Walter O. Krumbiegel Middle School • Hillside, NJ
Louise Meyer • School 4 • Clifton, NJ
Phyllis Mordente • Mountain View School • Mendham, NJ
Dan Rose • Hebrew Academy of Morris County • Randolph, NJ
Joy Spevak • Tinc Road School • Flanders, NJ
Beth Warren • Robert Frost School • East Brunswick, NJ

Product Concept: Planned Productions

2 3 4 5 6 PP 10 09 08 07 06

For information, contact
Perfection Learning® Corporation
1000 North Second Avenue, P.O. Box 500
Logan, Iowa 51546-0500
Phone: 1-800-831-4190 • Fax: 1-800-543-2745

#79915 ISBN 0-7891-6516-3

To the Student

This book will help you review, practice, and master the New Jersey Reading Core Curriculum Content Standard and Cumulative Progress Indicators. Here are the steps to follow to use this book.

1. Take the Tryout Test and check your answers. Use the chart at the bottom of this page to find out your strengths and weaknesses in the areas covered. Don't be discouraged if you don't get all the answers right or if you don't understand some questions. Remember the questions that are hard for you to answer. They will be the types of questions you need to work on the most.

2. Work through the lessons that follow the Tryout Test. Each lesson reviews example items and provides a practice test based on the progress indicators. Fill in the Keeping Score chart on page 99 as you complete each practice test.

3. After completing all the lessons, take the Mastery Test. Your score on this test will show your understanding of the Reading Core Curriculum Content Standard and Cumulative Progress Indicators.

By following the steps outlined above, you will increase your mastery of the New Jersey Reading Core Curriculum Content Standard and Cumulative Progress Indicators.

Lesson	Tryout Test Items	Mastery Test Items
1 Text Features	12, 13, 19	18, 26, 29
2 Word Recognition	7, 17, 27, 30	5, 24
3 Reading Strategies	10, 33	16, 31
4 Vocabulary Skills	5, 6, 26, 32	6, 14, 19, 20, 25
5 Evaluating What You Read	11, 18, 28, 31, 34, 35	17, 21, 27, 28, 32
6 Comprehension Strategies	14, 15	3, 22, 23
7 Reading Literature	1, 4, 16, 20	8, 11, 12, 30
8 Literary Elements	2, 3, 8, 9	1, 2, 4, 9, 13
9 Literary Devices and Structures	21, 22, 23, 24, 25, 29	7, 10, 15, 33, 34, 35

Table of Contents

To the Student 2

Lessons and Tests

Tryout Test This test will tell you how well you understand New Jersey's Core
Curriculum Content Standard for reading *before* using this book 4

Concepts About Print/Text

1 **Text Features** (A1–A2)
Use a text index and glossary and survey and explain text features 18

Decoding and Word Recognition

2 **Word Recognition** (C1–C4)
Use phonics, syllabication, affixes, spelling rules, context clues, and the
pronunciation key of a dictionary to decode and recognize new words 25

Reading Strategies

3 **Reading Strategies** (E4–E5)
Make revisions to text predictions during and after reading and apply
graphic organizers to illustrate key concepts and relationships in text 31

Vocabulary and Concept Development

4 **Vocabulary Skills** (F1–F5)
Infer word meanings from roots, affixes, and context clues; identify and use
antonyms, synonyms, homophones, and homographs; and use a dictionary
and a thesaurus 39

Comprehension Skills and Response to Text

5 **Evaluating What You Read** (G1, G5, G6, and G11)
Identify an author's purpose, views, and beliefs; recognize persuasive and
propaganda techniques, historical and cultural biases, and different points of
view; and identify and analyze text types, formats, and elements in nonfiction . . 46

6 **Comprehension Strategies** (G3 and G4)
Use cause and effect and sequence of events to gain meaning and anticipate
and construct meaning from text by making connections. 55

7 **Reading Literature** (G7–G10)
Recognize and understand themes; distinguish between major and minor
details; and make inferences and provide supporting evidence 63

8 **Literary Elements** (G2 and G12)
Identify genre and recognize literary elements in stories, including setting,
characters, plot, and mood 69

9 **Literary Devices and Structures** (G13–G15 and G17)
Identify the sound and structure of poetry; recognize figurative language;
interpret idiomatic expressions; and identify the structure of drama 77

Mastery Test This test will tell you how well you understand New Jersey's Core
Curriculum Content Standard for reading *after* using this book. 85

Keeping Score 99
Finding Percent 100
Tips for Taking Tests . . . . Inside Back Cover

Tryout Test

Estimated time: **60** minutes

Directions: Read the passage and answer the questions that follow.

On the Bus

by Pegi Bevins

1   Jarron was glad to be going home. For nine weeks he'd been riding the school bus, ever since he'd started at Ellington School. All that time he'd been pretty much alone.

2   Jarron didn't make friends easily. He was shy and self-conscious. At his last school, he'd been on the basketball team, so he had a few friends. But he had started at Ellington in March, when basketball season was over.

3   "Hey, I've told you guys before—no roughhousing," Mr. Marlin, the bus driver, called out, looking into his mirror. "I don't feel good today, so give me a break, huh?"

4   Jarron glanced back. The boys in the rear were clowning around. Jarron wished he could join them.

5   Suddenly the group burst out laughing. Someone had fallen into the aisle.

6   "Okay, Sanchez," Mr. Marlin said. "Sit here where I can see you." He pointed to the empty place next to Jarron.

7   Sanchez made his way to the front and sat down.

8   "Hey," Sanchez said, glancing at Jarron.

9   "Hey," Jarron answered. He hoped Sanchez would say more, but Sanchez was already turned around, making faces at his buddies.

10   Jarron sighed and looked out the window. His stop was on the other side of the river, and they were approaching the bridge.

11   "Ugh!"

12   Surprised, Jarron looked up and saw the driver slumped over the steering wheel. The bus lurched to the right, grazing the bridge's guardrail.

13   "Hey! What's going on?" someone yelled. Several kids screamed as the bus hit the median and then bounced to the right again.

14   Jarron had a clear view of Mr. Marlin and could see that he was unconscious with his foot on the gas pedal. The weight of it was making the bus go faster. Jarron <u>scrambled</u> up to him.

15   "Mr. Marlin!" he yelled, shaking the man's shoulder. No response.

16   The engine was racing even louder. With that kind of speed, they'd be over the railing in a matter of seconds.

17   "Grab the wheel!" someone yelled. "I'll get the brakes!"

18   Jarron looked down to see Sanchez beneath the dashboard. Jarron struggled for the wheel, pushing Mr. Marlin over until the man slumped against the window. He jerked the wheel to the left, away from the guardrail. The bus veered several times before Jarron could hold it steady.

19   The tires screeched as the brakes suddenly caught. Glancing down, Jarron saw that Sanchez had moved Mr. Marlin's foot and was throwing his full weight on the <u>brake</u> pedal. The bus jerked to a stop.

20   Almost instantly, two police officers appeared at the bus door.

21   "What happened?" one asked as Jarron opened the door.

22   "The driver had some kind of attack," Sanchez said, pointing at Mr. Marlin.

23   "I'll call an ambulance," the officer said. "Is anyone else hurt?"

24   One officer began checking Mr. Marlin's vital signs while the other checked for student injuries. He said that <u>arrangements</u> would be made to take everyone home.

25   "Hey, you've got some lightning-fast reactions!" Sanchez said to Jarron. "You're a hero, man." He punched Jarron playfully on the arm.

26   Jarron answered, "Well, if I'm a hero, you are too. You stopped the bus."

27   Sanchez smiled. "Yeah, I guess I did, didn't I?" He turned to rejoin his friends in the back. But just as Jarron was about to sit down, Sanchez stopped and said, "Hey, Superman, you want to come back here and wait with us?"

28   "Sure," Jarron replied. He hoped his ride wouldn't come too fast.

---

1 Which of the following sentences from the beginning of the story helps you guess that Jarron feels lonely?

Ⓐ *For nine weeks he'd been riding the school bus, ever since he'd started at Ellington School.*

Ⓑ *The boys in the rear were clowning around.*

Ⓒ *Jarron wished he could join them.*

Ⓓ *Suddenly the group burst out laughing.*

2 The main problem in the beginning of the story is that—

Ⓐ Jarron needs to make friends.

Ⓑ Mr. Marlin doesn't feel well.

Ⓒ Sanchez gets in trouble with the bus driver.

Ⓓ some of the boys are roughhousing.

3 Jarron's mood changes at the end of the story because—

    Ⓐ he had fun driving the bus.

    Ⓑ Sanchez has asked him to join the group.

    Ⓒ he wants to help the police officer.

    Ⓓ he will be going home soon.

4 A theme of the story is—

    Ⓐ people should behave on a bus.

    Ⓑ showing courage can help you make friends.

    Ⓒ a sudden illness can strike anyone.

    Ⓓ bus travel can be dangerous.

5 Read this sentence from the story.

Glancing down, Jarron saw that Sanchez had moved Mr. Marlin's foot and was throwing his full weight on the <u>brake</u> pedal.

Which of the following sentences uses the word <u>brake</u> in the same way?

    Ⓐ He knew the glass might ____ if he dropped it.

    Ⓑ There will be one ____ during the long test.

    Ⓒ She didn't want to ____ a promise.

    Ⓓ The bike's left ____ didn't work properly.

6 A synonym for <u>scrambled</u> in paragraph 14 is—

    Ⓐ paced.   Ⓒ mixed.

    Ⓑ confused.   Ⓓ hurried.

7 How many syllables are in the word <u>arrangements</u>?

    Ⓐ two   Ⓒ four

    Ⓑ three   Ⓓ five

8 The mood of the story during the bus emergency is—

    Ⓐ suspenseful.

    Ⓑ cheerful.

    Ⓒ sad.

    Ⓓ relaxed.

9 This story is an example of—

    Ⓐ historical fiction.

    Ⓑ a tall tale.

    Ⓒ realistic fiction.

    Ⓓ a myth.

10 Were you surprised when Sanchez invited Jarron to join his group in the end? Explain why or why not. Did your opinion of Sanchez change during the story? Use examples from the story to support your answer. (4 points)

_____

_____

_____

_____

_____

_____

_____

_____

_____

_____

_____

_____

_____

_____

_____

_____

_____

_____

Directions: Read the passage and answer the questions that follow.

The Invasion of Washington

Although the American Revolutionary War ended in 1783 and America was out from under Great Britain's rule, there were still disagreements between the two nations. British troops continued to occupy some forts and lands in America, and Britain had a policy of boarding U.S. ships to haul off British-born American sailors. Many American-born sailors were taken by mistake. These and other issues led America to declare war on Britain, launching the War of 1812. The following passage is from a book about the War of 1812. It describes a day toward the end of the war.

Battle of Bladensburg

In August 1814, a British **fleet** under the command of Admiral George Cockburn sailed up the Patuxent River. At Benedict, Maryland, the fleet unloaded about 4000 British troops and their leader General Robert Ross. This British force then started a 45-mile march toward Washington.

The Americans had destroyed the two bridges entering Washington from the east across the Potomac River. The British had to march about six miles northeast of the city and cross the bridge at Bladensburg. News of this threat immediately threw the capital's 8000 citizens into a panic!

Washingtonians ran in every direction. They loaded their belongings on wagons and poured out of the city. Many slave owners hid their slaves deep in the countryside, in the care of others. They wanted to hide their property from the British.

American General Winder put his **militia** in a good defensive position at the village of Bladensburg. Commodore Barney and his 500 sailors left their boats and reported for duty as infantry.

They hauled their ship's cannons with them and placed them in the middle of General Winder's defenses.

About noon on August 2, 1814, the British arrived and the Battle of Bladensburg began. American artillery thundered. The British aimed Congreve rockets at the American lines. When fired, these super weapons looked like giant <u>flaming</u> skyrockets and made shrill noises. Shrapnel shells from the rockets exploded while still in the air over the enemy. Then, sharp, deadly pieces of metal rained down.

Most of the American militia **lines** broke when faced with the rockets. Soldiers dropped their weapons and ran toward Washington.

Some militiamen stayed to fight. These soldiers joined Commodore Barney's sailors, who made a brave stand against the British forces. Soldiers on both sides were killed. But the British finally overtook the Americans. Commodore Barney was wounded and taken prisoner along with many of his troops.

The battle ended about four o'clock The British forces rested at Bladensburg a few hours before moving on to Washington, D.C.

Washington Under Attack

At about eight o'clock in the evening, the British army reached the outskirts of Washington. General Ross, Admiral Cockburn, and about 100 troops entered the city carrying a flag of truce. They had planned on telling the citizens that they would not be harmed. But a volley of shots ripped out from a house. General Ross's horse was shot.

The British were angry and felt the rules of warfare had been violated. They killed all the people in the house and burned it down. This was the only recorded incident of British violence against civilians.

The rest of the army then began burning down the government buildings in Washington. They set fire to the President's House, the Capitol, the Treasury Building, the Navy Yard, and several other important buildings.

This Washington inferno was so great that the glow in the night sky could be seen from 50 miles away. Fortunately, in the afternoon of the next day, a violent rainstorm swept over the city. It extinguished most of the flames in the public buildings.

This successful British attack on Washington, D.C., left most Americans feeling bitter and ashamed.

11 You can tell this passage is nonfiction because it—

Ⓐ has characters, a setting, and a plot.

Ⓑ gives information about real people and real events.

Ⓒ has a beginning, a middle, and an end.

Ⓓ has main ideas and details.

12 In the last paragraph the author—

Ⓐ introduces the Invasion of Washington.

Ⓑ briefly summarizes how Americans felt after the invasion.

Ⓒ explains how the British entered Washington.

Ⓓ explains how the Americans tried to defend their capital.

13 "Washington Under Attack" is—

Ⓐ the heading of one section of "The Invasion of Washington."

Ⓑ the title of a song about the War of 1812.

Ⓒ a phrase defined in the glossary.

Ⓓ the title of the entire passage.

GO ON

14 Look at the chart. It shows the order of some of the events of the invasion.

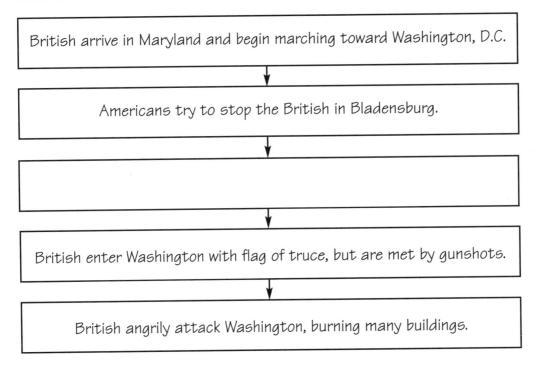

Which event belongs in the empty box?

Ⓐ British defeat Americans in Bladensburg and continue on to Washington.

Ⓑ British sail up the Patuxent River.

Ⓒ British burn the President's House and other buildings.

Ⓓ Americans destroy two of the bridges into Washington.

15 What caused the American soldiers to drop their weapons and run during the Battle of Bladensburg?

Ⓐ The British were marching toward Bladensburg.

Ⓑ Commodore Barney and his sailors left their boats.

Ⓒ The people of Washington were pouring out of the city.

Ⓓ The British fired deadly Congreve rockets.

16 Which detail does NOT belong in a summary of this passage?

Ⓐ The British had to march to Bladensburg to find a bridge to Washington.

Ⓑ The British used the Congreve rocket, a very deadly weapon.

Ⓒ The Battle of Bladensburg ended at about four o'clock.

Ⓓ The British entered Washington carrying a flag of truce.

17 The word <u>flaming</u> is formed by—

   Ⓐ adding the prefix *fla-* to the word *ming*.

   Ⓑ adding the suffix *-ing* to the word *flame* and dropping the *e*.

   Ⓒ adding the prefix *fl-* and the suffix *-ing* to the word *am*.

   Ⓓ combining the words *flam* and *ing*.

18 The purpose of this passage is to—

   Ⓐ persuade.

   Ⓑ entertain.

   Ⓒ give instructions.

   Ⓓ inform.

Use the glossary to answer question 19.

Glossary

alliance	joining of common interests among nations
barge	flat-bottomed boat used to transport goods
cabinet	group of people who give advice to a leader
civilian	person who is not in the military
delegate	representative
fleet	group of warships
frontier	unsettled land on the edge of settled land
infantry	soldiers trained to fight on foot
line	area where troops assemble to battle
looting	seizing and carrying away, especially during a war
maritime	relating to the sea
militia	body of citizens organized to fight in a war if necessary
neutral	not taking sides in a war

19 A <u>fleet</u> is—

   Ⓐ anything relating to the sea.

   Ⓑ a type of warship.

   Ⓒ a type of gun.

   Ⓓ a group of warships.

GO ON

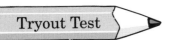
Directions: Read this page from a Web site about black history. Then use it and "The Invasion of Washington" to answer the questions that follow.

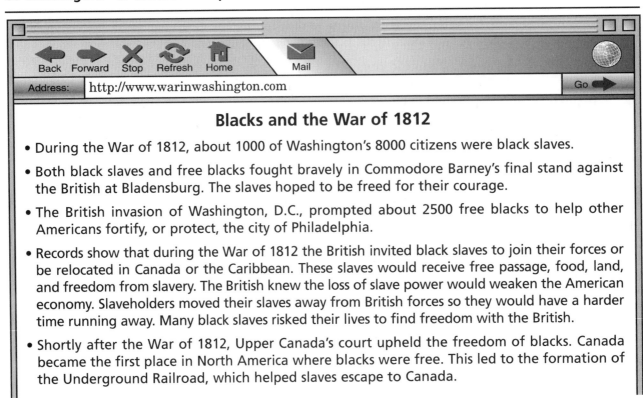

Blacks and the War of 1812

- During the War of 1812, about 1000 of Washington's 8000 citizens were black slaves.

- Both black slaves and free blacks fought bravely in Commodore Barney's final stand against the British at Bladensburg. The slaves hoped to be freed for their courage.

- The British invasion of Washington, D.C., prompted about 2500 free blacks to help other Americans fortify, or protect, the city of Philadelphia.

- Records show that during the War of 1812 the British invited black slaves to join their forces or be relocated in Canada or the Caribbean. These slaves would receive free passage, food, land, and freedom from slavery. The British knew the loss of slave power would weaken the American economy. Slaveholders moved their slaves away from British forces so they would have a harder time running away. Many black slaves risked their lives to find freedom with the British.

- Shortly after the War of 1812, Upper Canada's court upheld the freedom of blacks. Canada became the first place in North America where blacks were free. This led to the formation of the Underground Railroad, which helped slaves escape to Canada.

20 In "The Invasion of Washington" the author says that Washington slave owners rushed to hide their property (slaves) from the British. Why did they do this? Use information from the Web page to support your response. (4 points)

_____

_____

_____

_____

_____

_____

_____

_____

_____

_____

Directions: Read the poem and answer the questions that follow.

from "The Village Blacksmith"

by Henry Wadsworth Longfellow

Under a spreading chestnut-tree
The village smithy stands;
The smith, a mighty man is he,
With large and <u>sinewy</u> hands;
And the muscles of his brawny arms
Are strong as iron bands.

His hair is crisp, and black, and long,
His face is like the tan;
His brow is wet with honest sweat,
He earns whate'er he can,
And looks the whole world in the face,
For he owes not any man.

Week in, week out, from morn till night,
You can hear his bellows blow;
You can hear him swing his heavy sledge,
With measured beat and slow,
Like a sexton ringing the village bell,
When the evening sun is low.

And children coming home from school
Look in at the open door;
They love to see the flaming forge,
And hear the bellows roar,
And catch the burning sparks that fly
Like chaff from a threshing-floor.

21 Poets use words that create a rhythm, or beat. This poem's rhythm is—

Ⓐ lively and carefree.

Ⓑ soothing and gentle.

Ⓒ dramatic and hard to predict.

Ⓓ steady and easy to predict.

22 Reread the following line from the poem.

His hair is crisp, and black, and long

Which of the following choices has the same rhythm as the line above?

Ⓐ *His brow is wet with honest sweat*

Ⓑ *For he owes not any man*

Ⓒ *You can hear his bellows blow*

Ⓓ *Look in at the open door*

23 Which phrase best describes how the author organized this poem?

Ⓐ into stanzas of the same length, with no rhyming words

Ⓑ into stanzas of the same length, with a regular rhyming pattern

Ⓒ into stanzas of different lengths, with no rhyming pattern

Ⓓ into one long stanza, with a regular rhyming pattern

24 Which line has an example of alliteration?

Ⓐ *His brow is wet with honest sweat*

Ⓑ *They love to see the flaming forge*

Ⓒ *And hear the bellows roar*

Ⓓ *When the evening sun is low*

25 In the beginning of the poem the author compares the blacksmith's arms to—

Ⓐ iron bands.

Ⓑ a spreading chestnut tree.

Ⓒ crisp, black hair.

Ⓓ sweat.

GO ON

Directions: Use the dictionary entry and pronunciation key to answer questions 26 and 27.

sinew (sin′ yü) *n.* **1.** A strong, tough cord that joins muscle to bone; tendon: *He could see the sinews when he cut the cooked chicken.* **2.** Strength; energy; force: *We need a leader with much sinew.*

Pronunciation Key: pat, cāke, cãre, fär, less, ēqual, tėrm, it, nīce, lot, ōpen, ôrder, oil, out, cup, pu̇t, rüle, child, long, thin, **th**is, zh measure

ə represents **a** in about, **e** in taken, **i** in pencil, **o** in lemon, **u** in circus

26 The author describes the blacksmith's hands as <u>sinewy</u>. This means his hands have—

Ⓐ no tendons.

Ⓑ weak tendons.

Ⓒ strong, visible tendons.

Ⓓ been burned.

27 Which syllable should you stress when you say the word <u>sinew</u>?

Ⓐ both *sin* and *ew*

Ⓑ *sin*

Ⓒ *ew*

Ⓓ no syllable should be stressed

Directions: Read the passage and answer the questions that follow.

March 17

The Daily Gazette
Opinions and Editorials

Living Without Oil
by Alicia Carter

1   Oil is deadly to the environment. We should stop using it now. People argue that oil and oil products are important to the United States economy. They say that without oil, we would have no more rubber tires, CDs, or two-liter soda bottles. These products are all made from petroleum. I say we should learn to live without these things.

2   Oil is dangerous to the environment. Oil tankers often have accidents, and the oil they carry spills all over the ocean. Animals can be seriously hurt or even die because of oil spills. The oil gets on the beaches and ruins them. It costs a lot of money to clean up an oil spill. If we stopped using oil, there would be no more oil spills, so our environment would be cleaner.

3   Some people might think they don't use very much oil. They might think that they only use oil when they drive their cars. The fact is, people use more oil than they think. Around the world, people use nearly 6000 products made from petroleum. Many of them can be found in your home. The carpet on your floor, the paint on your walls, and the plastic in your toys all probably contain oil. You might even be wearing oil because many fabrics have fibers that contain chemicals made from—you guessed it—oil!

4   Americans use more than 25% of the oil that is produced in the world, but we produce only 13% of the world's total oil. At the rate we are using it, it is easy to see that someday we will run out of oil. What will we do then? We need to find different sources of energy now. If we wait until we run out of oil, we will really be in hot water. Our cars will be useless and there will be no way to keep our homes warm. We must act now!

5   The first thing we must do is reduce the amount of oil we use every day. There are some easy ways to do this. We should all ride bicycles, carpool, and take the bus instead of driving our cars. We can make sure we always wear clothing made of natural fibers such as cotton and wool. Some things are more difficult to do. For example, we should stop buying plastic products and rubber tires. Some people may think this is too difficult. However, we must do these things to save our environment. Let's all work together to save our Earth!

28 The author believes that—

Ⓐ oil is safe to use, but too expensive.

Ⓑ we should try to stop using oil.

Ⓒ oil causes minor problems.

Ⓓ we must find more oil.

29 Read the following sentence from paragraph 4.

If we wait until we run out of oil, we will really be in hot water.

To be in hot water means to be—

Ⓐ standing in a pool of hot water.

Ⓑ very angry.

Ⓒ in trouble.

Ⓓ very comfortable and safe.

30 As used in paragraph 5, the word fiber means—

Ⓐ grain.

Ⓑ texture.

Ⓒ color.

Ⓓ thread.

31 This passage is an example of a(n)—

Ⓐ book chapter.

Ⓑ editorial in a newspaper.

Ⓒ encyclopedia article.

Ⓓ advertisement.

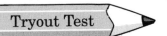

32 Read the thesaurus entry for <u>easy</u>.

> **EASY**
> *adjective*
>
> **simple** Not difficult. *It was a simple task.*
>
> **calm** Relaxed. *His calm manner helped the children relax.*
>
> **comfortable** Free of worry. *The wealthy man led a comfortable life.*
>
> **lenient** Not strict. *Mr. Smith is a lenient teacher.*

Which word is the best replacement for <u>easy</u> in paragraph 5?

Ⓐ simple   Ⓒ comfortable

Ⓑ calm   Ⓓ lenient

33 Study the web. It shows one of the author's main ideas and the details that support the main idea.

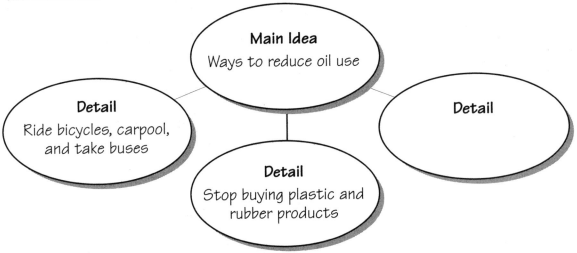

Which detail belongs in the empty box?

Ⓐ Wear clothing made of natural fibers.

Ⓑ People use nearly 6000 products made from petroleum.

Ⓒ Americans use more than 25% of the world's oil.

Ⓓ Oil tankers often have accidents.

34 The author tries to persuade the reader to stop using oil products by—

Ⓐ showing they are expensive.

Ⓑ showing they are not useful any longer.

Ⓒ making the reader feel that disaster will strike soon.

Ⓓ making the reader feel that oil products will be hard to give up.

35 Did the author convince you that it's important to stop using oil and oil products? Why or why not? Explain your answer using examples from the passage. (4 points)

_____

_____

_____

_____

_____

_____

_____

_____

_____

_____

_____

_____

_____

_____

_____

_____

_____

_____

_____

_____

STOP

Points Earned / Total = _____ / 44

Text Features

| This lesson covers . . . using a text index and glossary and surveying and explaining text features such as headings and introductory and concluding paragraphs. |

Directions: Read the passage. Then answer the questions that follow.

Saving the Oceans

1 We expect a lot from the ocean. The ocean gives us food, water, and energy. Yet what do we give the ocean in return? Unfortunately, people have caused serious problems in the oceans. Certain areas of the ocean have been overfished, damaging the **ecosystem**. We have also caused pollution that harms the plants and animals in the ocean.

Are There Plenty of Fish in the Sea?

2 Maybe you've heard the saying "there are plenty of fish in the sea." But in the case of the oceans, this saying isn't correct. Many areas of oceans have been overfished. This means that people have removed too many of a certain type of **marine** creature from the ocean. Overfishing harms the ocean. **Food chains** are broken and ecosystems are damaged.

3 Overfishing has occurred at the Grand Banks of Newfoundland. Too many of the cod were harvested. Young cod could not grow fast enough to replace the huge numbers of adult cod that were being caught. The great schools of cod disappeared. And the fish that ate the cod had suddenly lost a food source.

4 People from many different countries finally agreed to limit the number of fish taken from the Grand Banks. But even today, scientists are not sure if the fish in the area will ever recover from the overfishing.

Help! I'm Seasick!

5 If the ocean could speak, it might say that it is seasick. Pollution and waste are harming parts of the ocean. Some pollution runs into the ocean from streams and rivers on the continents. Other waste is dumped into the ocean. We also have created pollution while taking energy from underground oil wells.

6   Because the ocean is so large, it may seem as if the little amount of waste put into it wouldn't matter. But it does. Ocean creatures often swallow trash or get caught in it. Even small amounts of pollution can kill fish and ocean creatures.

7   The oceans cover much of the Earth. We must protect them from overfishing and pollution if we want to preserve the important ecosystems that live within their waters. Only then will they continue to thrive with life.

1 The purpose of paragraph 1 is to—

Ⓐ introduce the main problems in the oceans.

Ⓑ come to a conclusion about the health of the oceans.

Ⓒ explain some new words having to do with the ocean.

Ⓓ explain the dangers of overfishing.

2 The purpose of paragraph 7 is to—

Ⓐ introduce the main problems of the oceans.

Ⓑ briefly summarize why the oceans must be saved.

Ⓒ explain that the oceans cover much of the Earth.

Ⓓ explain how oceans become polluted.

3 In this passage, "Help! I'm seasick!" is—

Ⓐ a quote from a scientist about pollution.

Ⓑ the heading of the section about pollution in the ocean.

Ⓒ the title of the entire passage.

Ⓓ the heading of the section about overfishing.

In **Example 1**, you must explain the purpose of an **introductory paragraph**. The first paragraph briefly introduces the topic of *saving the oceans* by telling about the two main problems facing oceans today: overfishing and pollution. The purpose of this introductory paragraph is to *introduce the main problems of the oceans*. Choice Ⓐ is correct.

In **Example 2**, you must explain the purpose of the **concluding paragraph**. Concluding paragraphs usually summarize the main ideas of a text or a section of a text. In this passage, the purpose of the last paragraph is to *briefly summarize why the oceans must be saved*. Choice Ⓑ is correct.

Example 3 asks about one of the passage's **headings**. Authors often organize articles, essays, or book chapters into smaller sections. Headings are the titles of these sections and usually tell the main idea of that section. "Help! I'm Seasick!" tells the reader that the section will be about something that makes the ocean "sick," such as pollution. It is *the heading of the section about pollution in the ocean*. Choice Ⓑ is correct.

GO ON

Glossary

biome environment with unique features

community organisms that live together in a particular location

coral reef rocky area in warm, shallow ocean waters created from the remains of animals called polyps

ecosystem group of living creatures that interact with one another and their surroundings

environment set of conditions found in a certain area; surroundings

evaporate to change from a liquid to a gas

food chain the order of who eats whom in a community

marine having to do with the ocean or salt water

organism living thing

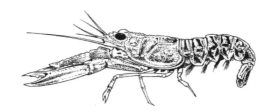

Index

ocean zones, 27–31
    midnight, 27, 31
    sunlit, 27, 28–29
    twilight, 27, 29, 31
overfishing, 33–34
Pacific Ocean, 13–14
plankton, 24
pollution, 34–35
Red Sea, 16
seas, 11
seaweed, 28
Southern Ocean, 11, 16–17
squid, 30
Tropic of Cancer, 23
Tropic of Capricorn, 23
upwelling, 24

4 To locate information in this book about twilight ocean zones, you should look on pages—

Ⓐ 27 and 31.

Ⓑ 33–34.

Ⓒ 27, 29, and 31.

Ⓓ 34–35.

5 An <u>ecosystem</u> is—

Ⓐ the order of who eats whom in a particular location.

Ⓑ a rocky area in warm, shallow ocean waters.

Ⓒ anything having to do with the ocean or salt water.

Ⓓ a group of living creatures that interact with one another and their surroundings.

An **index** is a detailed, alphabetical list of all topics in a book. Page numbers beside each topic tell where to find information about that topic in the book. In **Example 4**, you must use the book's index to locate information about twilight ocean zones. Since this topic is not found under *t* (for *twilight*), you should look under *o* for *ocean zones*. You'll notice there are several types of ocean zones listed, and *twilight* is one of them. Pages *27, 29, and 31* include information about twilight ocean zones. Choice Ⓒ is correct.

Example 5 asks you to find the meaning of *ecosystem*. In textbooks, a **bold** word within a sentence usually indicates the word is defined somewhere else in the book, such as in a **glossary**. This book's glossary defines *ecosystem* as *a group of living creatures that interact with one another and their surroundings*. Choice Ⓓ is correct.

Test-Taking Tips

1 Introductory paragraphs introduce the reader to the main topic of a book, chapter, or essay. Authors usually introduce a topic by briefly stating the main ideas. Sometimes, before stating the main ideas, an author may ask the reader questions. This helps readers think about their own experiences with the topic. Other times authors may begin by describing an object or situation. This helps the reader visualize, or "see," the topic.

2 At the end of the book, chapter, or essay, an author usually summarizes the main ideas and important details that were discussed. In this last, concluding paragraph, the author may also draw a conclusion or give an opinion about the topic. The details in the passage should help support the conclusion.

3 A section heading explains what information you can expect to find in the section that follows. It can help you understand the main idea of the section. If you are looking for specific information in a book, section headings will help guide your research. Scanning the headings before you read a chapter is a good reading strategy.

4 Some topics in an index are listed under a more general topic. For instance, in a book about animals, *poodles* may be listed under the more general topic *dogs*.

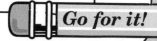

Go for it!

Test Practice 1: Text Features

Estimated time: **15** minutes

Directions: Read the book chapter. Then use the chapter, glossary, and index to answer the questions.

Chapter 4

Copying Nature

1 Nature is full of amazing and useful objects. But when natural objects aren't practical to use, humans must invent their own. Throughout history we have copied ideas from nature's plants and animals to make new inventions. Two interesting **textiles**—Velcro and fleece fabrics—were invented using ideas from nature.

Velcro

2 Have you ever walked through a field full of weeds? If there are cockleburs in that field, you'll bring some home with you. Cockleburs are weeds that stick to clothes.

3 In 1948, a Swiss man named George de Mestral found some cockleburs on his clothes and his dog. They were hard to pick off. He decided to find out why they were so pesky. He put one under a microscope. He saw many little burrs, or hooks, sticking out from the center. Those hooks helped the cocklebur grab and stick to fur and loops in fabric.

4 De Mestral thought that there must be a way to use this idea to make a fastener. He experimented for years. Then he finally did it! He found a way to make matching strips of fabric that hold tight like cockleburs but that come apart easily. One fabric strip had small fuzzy loops, and the other side had many small stiff hooks like the cocklebur. When the two strips were pressed together, they held tightly. But they could be pulled apart and reused.

5 De Mestral named his hook-and-loop fastener Velcro. The word is a combination of two words—*velvet*, a soft, **plush** fabric, and *crochet*, a type of needlework that uses a special hook

to make a series of loops. Today Velcro is often used instead of buttons, zippers, and laces. You can find it on shoes, in NASA space shuttles, and even in artificial hearts.

Fleece

6   The wool fleece from sheep is fluffy, warm, and soft. After a sheep is trimmed, the fleece grows back.

7   Polyester fleece was made to look like wool fleece, but large amounts of crude oil were used in the process. In 1993, textile makers discovered a way to save oil and make fleece fabrics. They used recycled plastic soda bottles!

8   Companies collect thousands of plastic bottles and chop them into tiny flakes. The flakes are cleaned, melted, and pushed through a **spinneret** to make long **fibers**.

9   Bales of fiber are sent to **mills**.

There, the fibers are knit and dyed to make a soft, fluffy fabric. Synchilla and Polarfleece are two common names for this "recycled" fleece.

10   It takes 3700 2-liter bottles to make enough Synchilla for 150 items of clothing. That's lots of plastic. But that saves 42 gallons of crude oil and creates less air pollution.

11   Mountain-climbing clothes, hats, and jackets are made from these fleecy fabrics. They keep people warmer than real sheepskin and cost less.

12   Nature's own products often can't be beat. They have kept us comfortable and safe throughout our history. But copying nature to make new inventions often has surprisingly good results. Sometimes scientists can make a new product that is cheaper and even better than the natural one. These human-made products may help more people.

Glossary

fiber fine thread of a natural or synthetic material, such as cotton or nylon, that can be spun into yarn

loom hand- or machine-operated device for weaving thread or yarn into cloth

mill building used for processing raw materials and manufacturing a product such as fabric or paper

natural present in or produced by nature

plush having long, soft fibers that stick up slightly from the surface of a fabric such as velvet

spinneret device for making filaments of synthetic fiber consisting of finely perforated plates through which liquid passes

synthetic made artificially by a chemical process

textile cloth or fabric that is woven, knitted, or otherwise manufactured

GO ON

Index

jeans, 4, 6, 17–19, 27
Kevlar, 4, 25
knitting, 16
lanolin, 7
natural fibers, 7–10
    cotton, 5–6, 11, 12, 15–19, 22, 25–30
    jute, 5, 7
    linen, 5, 6–7, 29, 30
    silk, 5, 9–10, 11, 22, 23
    wool, 5, 7–8, 13, 22–25, 29, 30
Nomex, 25
nylon stockings, 11, 22–23
renewable natural resources, 11
rope, 10, 24, 25, 26
Strauss, Levi, 17–18
sun-resistant clothing, 27

1   A textile is—

  Ⓐ something that copies nature.

  Ⓑ a hand- or machine-operated device for weaving thread or yarn into cloth.

  Ⓒ cloth or fabric that is woven, knitted, or otherwise manufactured.

  Ⓓ anything that keeps people warm and comfortable.

2   The purpose of paragraph 1 is to—

  Ⓐ make a conclusion about inventing new products.

  Ⓑ introduce the main ideas of the chapter.

  Ⓒ explain how to find useful objects in nature.

  Ⓓ define some of the words used in the chapter.

3   Paragraphs 2 through 5 are mainly about—

  Ⓐ cockleburs.

  Ⓑ Velcro.

  Ⓒ fleece.

  Ⓓ copying nature.

4   In this book, you can find information about rope on—

  Ⓐ page 16.

  Ⓑ pages 7–10.

  Ⓒ pages 5, 9–10, 11, 22, 23.

  Ⓓ pages 10, 24, 25, 26.

5   According to the index, silk is—

  Ⓐ one type of natural fiber.

  Ⓑ made artificially by a chemical process.

  Ⓒ a kind of rope.

  Ⓓ one type of synthetic fiber.

6   If the author were to include another invention in chapter 4, it would be an invention that—

  Ⓐ copied nature.

  Ⓑ was made of fleece.

  Ⓒ was made in a mill.

  Ⓓ was completely natural.

7   In paragraph 12, the author concludes the chapter by saying—

  Ⓐ natural products are always better.

  Ⓑ human-made products may help more people than natural ones do.

  Ⓒ copying nature rarely works.

  Ⓓ human-made products are more expensive than natural ones are.

STOP

Points Earned/Total = _____/7

Word Recognition

This lesson covers . . . using phonics, syllabication, prefixes, suffixes, spelling rules, context clues, and the pronunciation key of a dictionary to decode and recognize new words.

Directions: Read the passage and answer the questions that follow.

This passage is from a story about Joshua, a twelve-year-old slave trying to escape from his master in the 1850s. He is heading north toward a state that does not allow slavery. In this passage, a wagon driver offers to help Joshua.

Joshua <u>slowed</u> when daybreak <u>arrived</u>. Walking alone might invite a slave catcher. Had Master Scott put out a reward for him yet?

At the top of the hill, Joshua saw a wish on wheels—a <u>Conestoga</u> wagon. It wasn't a simple, flat, platform rig like Master Scott had. This wagon was as blue as the night sky. Its thick wheels could cut through the worst mud. The body was rounded a bit like a boat. An apple-red framework <u>supported</u> the wagon bottom. The white canvas roof made it look as though clouds covered the wagon.

Joshua ducked behind a tree trunk to admire the dream wagon. The four steam-snorting horses pulling the wagon <u>stopped</u> near the tree. Joshua thought about leaping to safety in the treetop. But before he could move, the wagon driver spoke.

"Greetings, friend!"

Joshua's mouth dropped open. "Pardon me, sir?"

The man had skin lighter than Master Scott's. But Master Scott had never smiled so <u>sincerely</u>.

The driver laughed. "Yes, you heard me right. Friends will be waiting to greet you up North. But we must leave now."

Joshua needed only three bounces to land on the wagon seat. "I'm Joshua Chandler. I am, uh, I . . .Well, who are you?"

The driver smiled. "Do not question me, and I'll not lie to you. You may be safer not knowing your friends."

Joshua nodded slowly.

"Ya! Ya!" the driver called. The horses obeyed.

"I have apples in back," the driver said. "I sell my pickings to the river boat travelers. I hope to do business in <u>Memphis</u>. Your future may rest on one of the steamships in port there."

Joshua nodded. Wagons. Steamships. How fast could he reach freedom? His mind was racing faster than any machine.

GO ON

1 In which of the following words does the ending *-ed* form a new syllable?

Ⓐ slowed
Ⓑ arrived
Ⓒ supported
Ⓓ stopped

Use the dictionary entry for <u>Conestoga</u> and the pronunciation key to answer questions 2 and 3.

2 Which syllable of Conestoga has a long "o" sound?

Ⓐ the first syllable
Ⓑ the second syllable
Ⓒ the third syllable
Ⓓ the fourth syllable

Conestoga (kon-ə-stō´-gə) *n*. A covered wagon with broad wheels used to cross the prairies of the United States in the 1800s.

3 Which syllable should you stress when you say <u>Conestoga</u>?

Ⓐ the first syllable
Ⓑ the second syllable
Ⓒ the third syllable
Ⓓ the fourth syllable

Pronunciation Key: pat, cāke, cãre, fär, less, ēqual, tėrm, it, nīce, lot, ōpen, ôrder, oil, out, cup, pu̇t, rüle, child, long, thin, <u>th</u>is, zh measure

ə represents **a** in about, **e** in taken, **i** in pencil, **o** in lemon, **u** in circus

4 The word <u>sincerely</u> is formed by—

Ⓐ adding the suffix *-ly* to the word *sincere*.
Ⓑ adding the prefix *since-* to the word *rely*.
Ⓒ combining the words *since* and *rely*.
Ⓓ adding the suffix *-rely* to the word *since*.

5 Which word has the same sound as the underlined letters in *Mem<u>ph</u>is*?

Ⓐ pitch
Ⓑ plant
Ⓒ his
Ⓓ fill

6 Read the following sentence from a different part of the story.

A <u>tear</u> rolled down Joshua's cheek.

Choose the word that rhymes with <u>tear</u> as it is used in the sentence.

Ⓐ bear
Ⓑ care
Ⓒ fear
Ⓓ fare

In **Example 1**, you must show your understanding of **rules about spelling and syllables**. Usually, adding *-ed* to a word to create the past tense does *not* create a new syllable. But when the base word ends in a *t* or a *d*, then adding *-ed does* make a new syllable. The word *supported* is the only choice that has a base word ending in *t* or *d*. Adding the ending *-ed* to *support* forms a new syllable. The ending *-ed* did not form a new syllable when it was added to the other words. Choice © is correct.

This chart shows some rules about breaking words into syllables. These rules may help you pronounce a new word.

Syllabication Rule	Example
Every syllable has one vowel sound.	home sub ject
A compound word is divided between the two words that make the compound word.	day break frame work
When a vowel is sounded alone in a word, it usually forms its own syllable.	a pron u nit
A prefix usually forms its own syllable.	mis fit un tie
A suffix usually begins a new syllable.	kind ness thank ful
When *-ed* comes at the end of a word, it forms its own syllable *only* when the root word ends in *t* or *d*.	root ed hand ed

This chart shows some common spelling rules that may help you read a new word.

Spelling Rule	Root	Example
Nouns ending in a consonant and a *y*, change *y* to *i* when adding *es*.	family	families
Nouns ending in a vowel and a *y*, just add *s*.	monkey	monkeys
Words ending in *e*, drop the final *e* before adding a suffix beginning with a vowel.	care	caring
Words ending in *ie*, change the *ie* to a *y* before adding a suffix.	lie	lying
Some words ending in *y*, change *y* to *i* before adding suffixes beginning with vowels.	bury	burial
Some words ending in *f*, change the *f* to *v* and add *-es*.	calf	calves
Words of one syllable ending in a single consonant preceded by a single vowel, double the final consonant before adding *-ed* and *-ing*.	trim	trimming
Words of one syllable ending in a single consonant preceded by a double vowel, just add *-ed* and *-ing*.	room	rooming

Example 2 tests your ability to use a dictionary's **pronunciation key**. Beside each word in a dictionary you will find its pronunciation in parentheses. This is called a *pronunciation guide*. The word is broken into syllables, and special symbols show how to say each syllable. A dictionary's pronunciation key explains the symbols by giving examples of common words with those sounds. The pronunciation key in this example shows that ō represents the long "o" sound, as in *ōpen*. The *o* in the third syllable of *Conestoga* has this sound. Choice Ⓒ is correct.

Example 3 tests your understanding of accent marks in a pronunciation guide. Pronunciation guides show you which syllable to stress when you say a word. An accent mark after a syllable means that syllable is stressed when the word is spoken. The accent mark for *Conestoga* falls after the *sto* syllable. Choice Ⓒ is correct.

In **Example 4**, you must use your knowledge of **prefixes** and **suffixes** to read the word *sincerely*. Adding the suffix *-ly* to the word *sincere* forms the word *sincerely*. Choice Ⓐ is correct.

In **Example 5**, you must use knowledge of **phonics** to read the word *Memphis*. The letters *ph* in *Memphis* make the same sound as the letter *f*. The only word that has the same sound is *fill*, choice Ⓓ.

In **Example 6**, you must use **context clues** to read the word *tear* correctly. Context clues are other words in a sentence or nearby sentence that help you understand a new word. There are two ways to pronounce *tear*, and each has its own meaning. It can mean *to pull apart by force*, as in *Don't tear the paper*. When we use this meaning of *tear*, it rhymes with *bear*. But the word *tear* can also mean a *drop of water from the eye*. This *tear* makes the most sense in the sentence about Joshua. The word that rhymes with this *tear* is *fear*, choice Ⓒ.

Test-Taking Tips

1 Adding a prefix or suffix to a word creates a new word. Becoming familiar with common prefixes and suffixes can help you read these new words. Adding a suffix sometimes changes the spelling of a root word. Reviewing the spelling rules about adding suffixes may help you understand how the root word has changed. This may help you recognize the word.

2 Forming a plural sometimes requires a spelling change. Letters may be added, removed, or replaced by others. Reviewing spelling rules will help you recognize when a familiar word has been made into a plural.

Go for it!

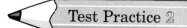

Test Practice 2: Word Recognition

Estimated time: **12** minutes

Directions: Read the passage and answer the questions that follow.

Now continue reading about the young runaway slave, Joshua.
In this passage, the kind wagon driver tries to hide Joshua's identity from
a bounty hunter. In the 1800s, bounty hunters were hired to find runaway
slaves and return them to their owners.

1   Joshua's smooth ride soon turned into a bumpy nightmare.

2   The whip cracked. The horses <u>swerved</u>. The wagon skidded off the road.

3   Suddenly the driver <u>shoved</u> Joshua off the seat. He tumbled into the back of
the apple-filled wagon.

4   "Hey!" Joshua complained.

5   "Down and quiet, friend!" the driver <u>hissed</u>. His wagon <u>glided</u> into a thicket of
trees. "We may have company."

6   Joshua bent down in the apple-sweet darkness. A minute or two passed in
silence. Finally, the quiet coaxed him to peek out the back of the wagon cover.

7   The driver grabbed Joshua. He hurled the boy into a muddy clearing. Joshua
struggled to his feet.

8   When Joshua <u>regained</u> his balance, he wiped the mud from his eyes and ears.
He could see the stranger approaching.

9   "I am John Bush," the stranger growled. "Matthew Scott is missing a slave."
Joshua saw the man on horseback <u>tapping</u> a pistol tucked in his belt. "Is this the
runaway?"

10   The driver laughed. "I am Robert Welborn. This is my son, David. The boy
<u>wrestled</u> a hornet's nest and lost. The mud eases his pain."

11   Joshua remained quiet, frozen in fear.

12   The bounty hunter boomed with laughter. "This bug wrestler doesn't look like
any boy I seek. However, a reward is offered for the return of a slave boy. I can
share such pay with anyone who helps my search. Good day, Mr. Welborn."

13   The driver waved at the <u>retreating</u> bounty hunter. Then he fetched Joshua
from the mud. "Forgive me. You'll find a brook behind those bushes."

14   Joshua washed himself and his clothes. Then he crouched behind some bushes
to wait. His mystery friend brought him some apples to dine on in the bushy
<u>hideaway</u>.

15   "I must go on alone," the man whispered into the bushes. "When your clothes
are dry, dress and walk up the road to the hilltop. The Mississippi River awaits
on the other side of the hill. We cannot speak again. Good luck, friend."

GO ON

Use the dictionary entry for <u>hideaway</u> and the pronunciation key to answer question 1.

1 Which syllable is stressed in <u>hideaway</u>?

   Ⓐ hide

   Ⓑ a

   Ⓒ way

   Ⓓ all syllables

hideaway (hīd´-ə-wā) *n.* **1.** A place in which to hide. **2.** A place to relax, away from others.

Pronunciation Key: pat, cāke, cãre, fär, less, ēqual, térm, it, nīce, lot, ōpen, ôrder, oil, out, cup, pủt, rüle, child, long, thin, this, zh measure

ə represents **a** in about, **e** in taken, **i** in pencil, **o** in lemon, **u** in circus

2 Which of the following words from the story has two syllables?

   Ⓐ swerved

   Ⓑ shoved

   Ⓒ hissed

   Ⓓ glided

3 The prefix in the word <u>regained</u> is—

   Ⓐ ed.   Ⓒ re.

   Ⓑ gain.   Ⓓ gained.

4 The word <u>tapping</u> is formed by—

   Ⓐ combining the words *tap* and *ping*.

   Ⓑ adding the prefix *tap-* to the word *ping*.

   Ⓒ adding the suffix *-ping* to the word *tap*.

   Ⓓ adding the suffix *-ing* to the word *tap* and doubling the consonant *p*.

5 Which word has the same sound as the underlined letters in <u>wrestler</u>?

   Ⓐ willow

   Ⓑ which

   Ⓒ rant

   Ⓓ claw

6 Read the following sentence from another part of the story.

   He hoped the man would <u>lead</u> him to a safe place.

   Choose the word that rhymes with <u>lead</u> as it is used in the sentence.

   Ⓐ bead

   Ⓑ bread

   Ⓒ dead

   Ⓓ head

7 How many syllables does <u>retreating</u> have?

   Ⓐ one

   Ⓑ two

   Ⓒ three

   Ⓓ four

STOP

Points Earned/Total = _____ /7

30

Reading Strategies

This lesson covers . . . making revisions to text predictions during and after reading and applying graphic organizers to illustrate key concepts and relationships in text.

Directions: Read each part of the story and answer the questions that follow.

Carmen and Raul

Part 1

1   Carmen came home from middle school and emptied her backpack on the table. "Boy, do I have a lot of homework," she said to herself. "It's going to take me hours to get it all done. I'd better get to work."

2   Carmen sat down and opened up her social studies book. She had read about one paragraph of her assignment when her little brother Raul ran into the room. Though Raul was in third grade, he never seemed to have any homework.

3   "Hi, Carmy," he said excitedly. "Want to come and play baseball with me? I just learned a new way to hold the bat, and . . ."

4   Carmen started to feel angry. No matter how much schoolwork she had, Raul always wanted her attention. Couldn't he see all her books scattered on the table? Didn't he realize that she was very busy? Wasn't there some reading or studying that he should be doing?

1   Based on what you have read so far, Carmen will probably—

Ⓐ give Raul a hug.

Ⓑ ask Raul to run some errands for her.

Ⓒ organize a neighborhood baseball game.

Ⓓ tell Raul she's too busy to play.

Part 2

5   The thing was, though, Carmen felt responsible for her brother. She had promised her parents to keep an eye on him when they weren't around. Maybe one quick game of pitch-and-hit wouldn't hurt.

6   Carmen gave a big sigh and closed her social studies book. "Okay, Raul. I'll play with you for a little while," she said. Once again, her schoolwork would have to wait.

7   After half an hour of baseball, Raul decided to play video games. Carmen had to put her fingers in her ears to keep his excited screams from distracting her. She wondered if her brother would ever learn to sit silently and just read.

2 After reading Part 1, you may have predicted that Carmen would not play with Raul. Which words from Part 2 help you understand why Carmen ends up playing with Raul?

Ⓐ . . . *Carmen felt responsible for her brother.*

Ⓑ *Carmen gave a big sigh . . .*

Ⓒ *"I'll play with you for a little while."*

Ⓓ . . . *her schoolwork would have to wait.*

Part 3

8 The next day when Raul came home from school, though, he was surprisingly quiet. He didn't talk about playing baseball or video games. In fact, he didn't really talk at all. He just went into his bedroom and lay down on the bed. When Carmen came in to see him, she thought he looked very pale.

9 Dad took Raul to the doctor when he got home, and they found out that Raul had bronchitis as well as a fever. The doctor said he should stay home from school for the rest of the week. Grandma Perez came to stay with him during the day.

10 Now when Carmen came home from school, she would have peace. No one would distract her as she studied. But Carmen found that she couldn't concentrate. On the first day that Raul was in bed, she got very little work done.

11 On the second day, Carmen went into her brother's room. "When do you think you'll be talking again?" she asked Raul. "I almost miss hearing your voice."

---

3 Look at the flow chart. It shows the order of the main events in the story.

Carmen feels annoyed when Raul wants to play.

↓

↓

Raul becomes ill, and Carmen looks forward to peace and quiet.

↓

Carmen can't concentrate when Raul is sick.

↓

Carmen realizes she misses her brother.

Which statement belongs in the empty box?

Ⓐ Carmen comes home from middle school.

Ⓑ Carmen feels responsible for Raul and agrees to play.

Ⓒ Carmen asks Raul when he'll be talking again.

Ⓓ Grandma Perez comes to watch Raul during the day.

4 Describe how Carmen's feelings about her brother change throughout the story. Why do they change? Use examples from the story to explain your answer. (4 points)

_____

_____

_____

_____

_____

_____

_____

_____

_____

_____

_____

_____

_____

5 Study the diagram.

Cause ⟶	Effect
Raul becomes sick and the house is very quiet.	

Which statement belongs under "Effect"?

Ⓐ Carmen gets a lot of homework done.

Ⓑ Grandma Perez leaves.

Ⓒ Carmen becomes angry.

Ⓓ Carmen learns to appreciate her brother.

When you read, you should use clues in the text—as well as what you already know—to predict what will come next. **Example 1** asks you to predict what will happen based on what you read in the first part of the story. There are several clues in Part 1 that show how Carmen feels. She has a lot of homework and feels angry that Raul doesn't seem to understand this. These clues lead you to predict that Carmen might _tell Raul she's too busy to play_. Choice Ⓓ is correct.

GO ON

Even though a prediction seems reasonable, it may not be correct. In **Example 2**, you must show which clue helps you **revise a prediction**. After reading Part 1, it seems likely that Carmen will not play with Raul. In Part 2, we learn that even though Carmen feels angry, her sense of responsibility causes her to agree to play with Raul. Choice Ⓐ, *Carmen felt responsible for her brother*, is correct.

Example 3 asks you to use a **graphic organizer** called a *flow chart*. Graphic organizers help you understand relationships between important ideas and events. A flow chart shows events in the order that they happen. It can help you see how one event leads to another. The event that belongs in the missing box is *Carmen feels responsible for Raul and agrees to play*, choice Ⓑ.

In **Example 4**, you must explain how Carmen's feelings for her brother change. A good response supports the explanation with examples from the story.

> **Good:** In the beginning of the story, Carmen feels angry with Raul. He wants her to play with him. But he doesn't seem to care that she is busy. Carmen also feels responsible for Raul and agrees to play anyway. She isn't happy about it, though.
>
> When Raul gets sick, Carmen's feelings change. At first she thinks the peace and quiet will help her get her work done. But it only makes her realize how much she misses Raul. She realizes how much she cares about him.

A poor response won't answer the questions thoroughly, or it may not use examples from the story for support.

> **Poor:** Carmen doesn't like Raul in the beginning. He is too noisy. She's angry, but plays with him anyway because she's supposed to.

In **Example 5**, another graphic organizer helps you understand the effect of Raul's illness on Carmen. The chart shows a cause (Raul's illness). You must complete the chart by choosing the effect. The effect of Raul's illness is that *Carmen learns to appreciate her brother*. Choice Ⓓ is correct.

Venn diagrams and webs are two other kinds of graphic organizers. Venn diagrams help you compare and contrast ideas, people, or events. Webs help you see how details support a main idea.

Test-Taking Tips

1 Titles, clues in the text, illustrations, important words, and things you already know can help you make predictions. As you read the story, try to revise your predictions based on new clues.

2 Before using a graphic organizer, think about what it is trying to show. Flow charts show events in order. Venn diagrams compare and contrast. Webs show main ideas and details.

Go for it!

Test Practice 3: Reading Strategies   Estimated time: **20** minutes

Directions: Read each part of the story and answer the questions that follow.

What Miriam Did
Part 1

There were five children in Miriam's family, and Miriam was the one in the middle. Benjamin, her older brother, had just received a college scholarship, and her older sister Rebecca was a star swimmer. Everyone paid attention to five-year-old Nathan and Joshua because they were identical twins. Miriam was just . . . Miriam. She helped her mother with the washing and cleaning, and she always kept an eye on the twins when her mother was out running errands. In the twelve years of her life, she had never felt in any way special.

Miriam wanted to change the situation. She wanted to do something that would get her noticed in the family. She decided to make a list of things she could do well.

Miriam thought and thought, but her list was pretty short. She liked to swim, but she was not as good as Rebecca. She could draw a little, but her father was a professional illustrator. Miriam thought it might be hard to impress him with her work.

She finally decided that maybe her best skill was writing. If she could just think of an interesting topic, she might be able to write a story for the school magazine. Then she could see her name in print.

1 What is the best prediction for what will happen next in the story?

Ⓐ Miriam will write a story and have it published in the school magazine.

Ⓑ Miriam will ask Rebecca to help her with swimming.

Ⓒ Miriam will realize that she cannot do anything very well.

Ⓓ Miriam will run away from home.

2 Which of the following helped you make your prediction?

Ⓐ Miriam's decision to make a list

Ⓑ the title of the story

Ⓒ Miriam's decision to think of a good story topic

Ⓓ the fact that there are five children in the family

Part 2

That afternoon, while her mother went to the grocery store, Miriam sat down at her desk in the basement and began thinking. She could write a composition about how Benjamin won the college scholarship. Or she could write a funny story about how their grandma scared Nathan and Joshua at Halloween. Or she could . . .

All at once, Miriam realized she was smelling gas. It seemed to be coming down the basement stairs from the kitchen. Where were Nathan and Joshua, anyway?

---

3 Which of the following is a clue that the story will go in a different direction than you originally predicted?

Ⓐ Miriam sits at her desk and begins to think of what to write.

Ⓑ She thinks of how Ben won the college scholarship.

Ⓒ She thinks of her grandma scaring her brothers at Halloween.

Ⓓ She smells gas and wonders where her younger brothers are.

Part 3

Miriam dropped her notebook and pen and ran up the stairs. Things were looking pretty scary in the kitchen. Nathan had turned on one of the burners on the stove. The flame hadn't gone on, and gas was escaping from the burner. Nathan and Joshua were sitting on the floor. They both seemed a little dizzy.

Miriam ran over, turned off the burner, and opened the back door. She led both boys out of the kitchen and onto the back porch. Then she called 911.

An ambulance arrived at the house just as Miriam's mother returned. The paramedics checked the boys over and said they were fine.

"Miriam!" said her mother. "I'm glad that you were so observant! Of all my children, you are by far the most responsible. Sometimes I think this family would not survive without you."

Miriam went down to the basement and thought some more about writing a story. Now, though, she knew she didn't have anything to prove.

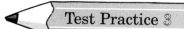

4 At the end of the story, why does Miriam say she has nothing to prove? Describe events in the story that cause Miriam to change her feelings about herself. (4 points)

_____

_____

_____

_____

_____

_____

_____

_____

_____

_____

_____

_____

_____

_____

_____

_____

_____

_____

5 Look at the flow chart. It shows the order of some of the events in the story.

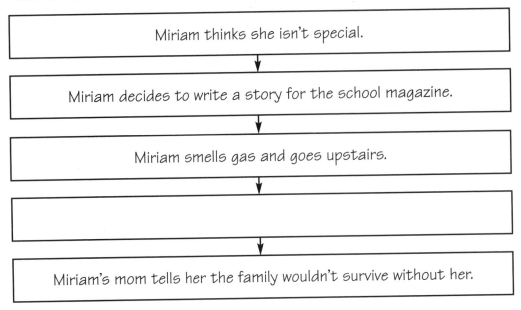

Which event belongs in the blank?

Ⓐ Miriam moves her brothers out of the house and calls for help.
Ⓑ Miriam makes a list of all the things she can do well.
Ⓒ Miriam goes down to the basement to think more about her story.
Ⓓ Miriam thinks it will be hard to impress her dad with her drawing.

6 Look at the following web. Supporting details surround a main idea from the story.

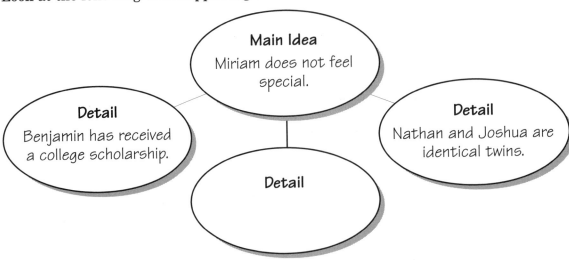

Which supporting detail from the story belongs in the empty box?

Ⓐ Miriam always keeps an eye on the twins.
Ⓑ Her father is a professional illustrator.
Ⓒ Miriam likes to draw.
Ⓓ Rebecca is a star swimmer.

STOP

Points Earned/Total = _____ /9

Vocabulary Skills

This lesson covers . . . inferring word meanings from learned roots, prefixes, suffixes, and context clues; identifying and correctly using antonyms, synonyms, homophones, and homographs; using a dictionary to define unknown words; and using a thesaurus to identify alternative word choices and meanings.

Directions: Read the passage. Then answer the questions that follow.

Fleeting Masterpieces

1   They are beautiful but <u>impermanent</u> art. Found in the distant villages of West Africa, they are some of the world's most dazzling wall paintings. Few people outside the villages will ever see them, however. The paintings decorate the walls of mud houses and last only from one rainy season to the next.

2   Women from such countries as Mauritania, Ghana, and Nigeria create these <u>fleeting</u> masterpieces. They use pigments, or colors, that come from local plants and clays. Their painting tools are simple: a clay bowl to hold the colored paste and a spoon handle or homemade brush to outline designs. With their <u>bare</u> hands, the women apply paint to large areas. The patterns they create are bold, <u>bright</u>, and meaningful, each telling something significant from the life of its maker. For instance, the painting might show a cooking pot, or it might repeat the pattern from a traditional cloth.

3   Most of these paintings are found on the outside walls of the village houses. However, some women of the Sominke tribe in Mauritania paint the inside of their houses because they spend so much time there. These women's villages are located on the edge of the Sahara Desert, where temperatures can reach 120°F by noon. The paintings provide welcome beauty in the <u>harsh</u> desert surroundings.

4   Sadly, the tradition of making wall paintings is disappearing. For generations, mothers handed down their expertise to their daughters. Now, however, many younger women are not responsive to learning old traditions. We can only hope that this unique and <u>beautiful</u> art form will survive for generations to come.

GO ON

1   In paragraph 1, <u>impermanent</u> means—

    Ⓐ lasting forever.
    Ⓑ lasting a short time.
    Ⓒ very important.
    Ⓓ not important.

2   In paragraph 2, <u>fleeting</u> means—

    Ⓐ short-lived.
    Ⓑ simple.
    Ⓒ very tiny.
    Ⓓ enormous.

3   Read the following sentence from the passage.

With their <u>bare</u> hands, the women apply paint to large areas.

Which of the following sentences uses <u>bare</u> in the same way?

    Ⓐ I can't ____ to look.
    Ⓑ The ____ is protecting her cubs.
    Ⓒ The cupboard was ____.
    Ⓓ This table can ____ a lot of weight.

4   Which word means the OPPOSITE of <u>bright</u> as it is used in paragraph 2?

    Ⓐ dull
    Ⓑ shiny
    Ⓒ cheerful
    Ⓓ brainless

5   Read the following dictionary entry for the word <u>harsh</u>.

> **harsh** (härsh) *adj.* **1.** Rough to the touch. **2.** Extremely
> unpleasant to the ears. **3.** Cruel, unkind: *a harsh man*.
> **4.** Severe, rugged, difficult: *a harsh climate or landscape*.

Which definition best fits the meaning of <u>harsh</u> as it is used in paragraph 3?

    Ⓐ definition 1
    Ⓑ definition 2
    Ⓒ definition 3
    Ⓓ definition 4

6 Read the thesaurus entry for <u>beautiful</u>.

> **BEAUTIFUL**
> *adjective*
>
> **cute** Pretty in a youthful way. *The girl looked cute with her hair in pigtails.*
>
> **lovely** Attractive. *She has a lovely smile.*
>
> **magnificent** Grand. *The tall oak trees looked magnificent.*
>
> **stunning** Strikingly attractive. *The woman looked stunning after her makeover.*

Which word would NOT be an appropriate replacement for <u>beautiful</u> in paragraph 4?

Ⓐ cute

Ⓑ lovely

Ⓒ magnificent

Ⓓ stunning

In **Example 1**, you must use familiar **roots**, **prefixes**, and **suffixes** to determine the meaning of *impermanent*. Prefixes are word parts added to the beginning of a root, or base, word. Suffixes are word parts added to the end of a root word. The prefix *im-*, which means "not" or "opposite of," has been added to the root word *permanent*. The word *impermanent*, then, means "not permanent," or *lasting a short time*. Choice Ⓑ is correct. Here are some common prefixes and suffixes, along with their meanings.

Prefixes	
Meaning	**Examples**
not	**dis**like, **un**like **im**polite, **il**legal
wrong or *badly*	**mis**fit, **mis**spell
for	**pro**-Democrat
against	**anti**war
before	**pre**heat
after	**post**game
between, among	**inter**office
under	**sub**way
again	**re**paint
across	**trans**oceanic

Suffixes	
Meaning	**Examples**
one who (does something)	paint**er**, sail**or**, art**ist**
state or quality of	amuse**ment**, sad**ness**, child**hood**, hero**ism**, toler**ance**, relat**ion**
of, like, or relating to	natur**al**, fac**ial**, suburb**an**, histor**ic** child**ish**, destruct**ive**
able to be	lov**able**, respons**ible**
filled with	care**ful**, marvel**ous**
without	care**less**

Example 2 asks you to use **context clues** to guess the meaning of the word *fleeting*. Context clues are the other words in a sentence or nearby sentences that help you understand an unfamiliar word. The first paragraph of the passage says that these paintings last only a brief time—from one rainy season to the next. This is a clue that *fleeting* means *short-lived*. Choice Ⓐ is correct.

In **Example 3**, you must tell the difference between the word *bare* and its **homophone**, *bear*. Homophones are words that are pronounced alike, but have different spellings and meanings. In choices Ⓐ, Ⓑ, and Ⓓ the word *bear* completes the sentences. Only in choice Ⓒ does the word *bare* complete the sentence. Choice Ⓒ, *The cupboard was (bare)*, is correct.

Example 4 asks you to find the **antonym** of *bright*. Antonyms are words with opposite meanings. In the sentence in paragraph 4, *bright* means "colorful." Its antonym is *dull*, choice Ⓐ.

Read the chart below. It explains synonyms, antonyms, homophones, and homographs.

Term	Definition	Example
synonyms	words that mean the same or nearly the same thing	cold / freezing
antonyms	words that mean the opposite	cold / hot
homophones	words that are pronounced the same but are spelled differently and have different meanings	to / too / two
homographs	words that are spelled the same but are pronounced differently and have different meanings	bow [bau] = the front part of a ship bow [bo] = a curved ribbon with a knot in the middle

In **Example 5**, you must use a **dictionary** to define the word *harsh*. The dictionary entry shows four different definitions. You must choose the definition that fits the sentence in the passage. The only definition that would describe a desert landscape is *definition 4,* severe, rugged, difficult: a harsh climate or landscape. Choice Ⓓ is correct.

In **Example 6**, you must use a **thesaurus** to replace the word *beautiful* with a similar word. A thesaurus is a book of synonyms. A thesaurus can help a writer find alternate word choices. The entry for *beautiful* lists four synonyms. Not all synonyms, however, work in all situations. You must choose one that is NOT an appropriate description of the African paintings. Based on words the author already has used to describe the paintings, *lovely*, *magnificent*, and *stunning* would all be appropriate choices. *Cute*, however, does not describe the paintings. Choice Ⓐ is correct.

Test-Taking Tips

1 If you cannot figure out the meaning of a word from its root, prefix, or suffix, look at the answer choices carefully. See which one makes the most sense in the sentence.

2 When determining the meanings of homophones and homographs, pay special attention to the context. Which meaning makes the most sense in the sentence?

3 When looking for antonyms (opposites), don't be fooled by choices that actually mean the same.

4 Context clues may not be in the same sentence as the underlined word. Look for clues in the sentences before and after the unknown word too. Sometimes you may need to read the entire passage before understanding a word.

5 When using a dictionary, pay close attention to the example sentences that follow a word's definition. Seeing the word in a sentence helps you understand the definition.

6 When using a thesaurus, think carefully about the message you are communicating. Not all synonyms work in every sentence.

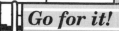 *Go for it!*

Test Practice 4: Vocabulary Skills

Estimated time: **15** minutes

Directions: Read the passage. Then answer the questions that follow.

The Story of King Midas

1   The god Bacchus, on a certain occasion, found his old schoolmaster and foster-father, Silenus, missing. The old man had wandered away and was found by some peasants, who carried him to Midas, their king. Midas recognized him and treated him with great hospitality, entertaining him for ten days and nights with an <u>unending</u> round of <u>jollity</u>. On the eleventh day Midas returned Silenus safely to Bacchus.

2   Whereupon Bacchus offered Midas his choice of a reward, whatever he might wish.

3   Midas thought for a moment and said, "I wish that everything I touch should be changed into gold."

4   Bacchus consented, though was sorry Midas had not made a better choice.

5   Midas went his way, rejoicing in his new power, which he hastened to put to the test. He could scarce believe his eyes when he found a twig of an oak, which when he plucked it from the branch became gold in his hand. He took up a stone; it changed to gold. He touched a blade of grass; it did the same. His <u>joy</u> knew no bounds, and as soon as he got home, he ordered the servants to <u>present</u> him with a splendid meal. Then he found to his dismay that when he touched bread, it hardened in his hand; or put a morsel to his lip, it <u>defied</u> his teeth.

6   Midas tried to <u>divest</u> himself of his power; he hated the gift he had requested. But his attempts were all in vain, and starvation seemed certain. He raised his arms, all shining with gold, in prayer to Bacchus. "Please," he begged, "deliver me from this glittering destruction!"

7   Bacchus, merciful <u>deity</u>, heard and agreed. "Go," said Bacchus, "to the source of the River Pactolus, plunge into the purifying water, and <u>wash</u> away your fault and its punishment."

8   Midas immediately followed the god's orders. As soon as he touched the water, the gold-creating power was given to the river. And the sands of the River Pactolus turned to gold, as they remain to this day.

---

1 The word <u>unending</u> in paragraph 1 means—

  Ⓐ about to end.

  Ⓑ seeming to never end.

  Ⓒ ending again.

  Ⓓ already ended.

2 The word in paragraph 1 that helps you understand the meaning of <u>jollity</u> is—

  Ⓐ *recognized.*

  Ⓑ *treated.*

  Ⓒ *great.*

  Ⓓ *entertaining.*

3 A word that means the OPPOSITE of <u>joy</u> is—

Ⓐ sadness. Ⓒ confusion.

Ⓑ fun. Ⓓ happiness.

4 Read this phrase from paragraph 5 of the story.

. . . he ordered the servants to <u>present</u> *him with a splendid meal.*

Which of the following sentences uses <u>present</u> in the same way?

Ⓐ He wished to live in the <u>present</u>, not the past.

Ⓑ It is my honor to <u>present</u> you with this award.

Ⓒ Every student was <u>present</u> that day.

Ⓓ The <u>present</u> situation is out of control.

5 Read the following dictionary entry for the word <u>defy</u>.

> **defy** (di-fī′) *v.* **-fied, -fying. 1.** To challenge someone to do something considered impossible: *The girl defied her friend to show the game was not fair.* **2.** To refuse to obey: *The child defied his father's rules.* **3.** To be beyond the powers of: *The strong army defied defeat.*

In the story, when Midas tried to bite a piece of golden food, it <u>defied</u> his teeth. This means that—

Ⓐ the food was beyond the powers of his teeth.

Ⓑ the food tasted very bitter.

Ⓒ his teeth were very sharp.

Ⓓ the food made his teeth very shiny.

6 In paragraph 6, <u>divest</u> means—

Ⓐ find. Ⓒ rid.

Ⓑ count. Ⓓ prove.

7 Read the following sentence from the story.

Bacchus, merciful <u>deity</u>, *heard and agreed.*

Which word from the first sentence of the story means the SAME as <u>deity</u>?

Ⓐ god

Ⓑ schoolmaster

Ⓒ foster-father

Ⓓ old

8 Read this thesaurus entry for the word <u>wash</u>.

WASH *verb*	
clean	To remove dirt from. *Please clean your hands before dinner.*
launder	To clean clothing. *I launder my socks and T-shirts using cold water.*
mop	To wipe using a brush on a long handle. *My weekly chore is to mop the kitchen floor.*
shampoo	To clean with soap and water. *We shampoo our dog's hair once a month.*

Which is the BEST word to replace <u>wash</u> as it is used in paragraph 7?

Ⓐ clean Ⓒ mop

Ⓑ launder Ⓓ shampoo

STOP

Points Earned/Total = _____/8

Evaluating What You Read

This lesson covers . . . identifying an author's purpose, views, and beliefs; recognizing persuasive and propaganda techniques, historical and cultural biases, and different points of view; and identifying and analyzing text types, formats, and elements in nonfiction.

Directions: Read the passage and answer the questions that follow.

Chapter 2

Exploring the Northeast

Hundred of years ago, explorers drifted in and around the Northeast region of North America. Vikings landed in what is now Maine and Rhode Island in 1000 A.D. In 1524, the Italian explorer Giovanni de Verrazzono sailed along much of the East Coast. In 1609, Henry Hudson explored the river eventually named for him. Dutch and English traders exchanged European goods for Native American furs.

Colonists

The first white people to settle in the Northeast were the Pilgrims. The Pilgrims left England in 1620 in search of religious freedom. After a long, hard journey across the Atlantic Ocean on the Mayflower, they reached the shore of the New World. They established Plymouth Colony in Massachusetts.

The Pilgrims found a new land rich in resources. Deer, caribou, black bears, bobcats, and turkeys ran through the woods. Trout and salmon filled the streams. The hills were covered with maple, birch, oak, beech, pine, and cedar trees.

The Pilgrims also met the native people of the land. The Wampanoag Indians were friendly and helpful at first. They taught the Pilgrims how to grow corn, squash, and beans and how to hunt for wild game.

Soon other groups sailed to the New World. In 1625, the Dutch founded New Amsterdam, which later became New York. In 1630, the Puritans arrived and founded Massachusetts Bay Colony. In 1681, William Penn, a Quaker from Britain, founded Pennsylvania.

As Europeans settled more land, the Wampanoags and other Native American tribes grew more <u>hostile</u>.* There were many conflicts over the ownership of the land. The colonists, who had superior weapons, often won these conflicts. Native Americans were forced to move to different areas.

---

*unfriendly, like an enemy

1 Describe how a Wampanoag Indian's version of these events would differ from this version. Would he or she use the word *hostile* to describe his or her tribe during the conflicts with the colonists? How might a Wampanoag Indian describe the colonists? Use examples from the passage to support your answer. (4 points)

_____

_____

_____

_____

_____

_____

_____

_____

_____

_____

_____

_____

_____

_____

_____

_____

_____

_____

_____

2 The author most likely wrote this passage to—

Ⓐ persuade people to visit Massachusetts.

Ⓑ tell a story about a Pilgrim family.

Ⓒ inform readers about early American history.

Ⓓ describe the landscape of the Northeast region.

3 You can tell this is nonfiction because it—

Ⓐ has characters, a setting, and a plot.

Ⓑ gives information about real people and real events.

Ⓒ has a beginning, a middle, and an end.

Ⓓ has main ideas and details.

Directions: Read the passages and answer the questions that follow.

Not Walker Lambert's Best Book
by Art Friedman

1   *The Mystery of Sleepy Lake* is a real yawn of a book. It features teenage sleuth Coleman Riley, the hero of two other books by Walker Lambert. In this newest yarn, Coleman finds a coded message hidden inside an abandoned rowboat. By decoding the message, he learns about a ring of thieves operating from a nearby cabin. Next, Coleman spies on the thieves and tries to foil their plans to rob the Sleepy Lake Motel. I won't give away more of the plot, although it proceeds about as predictably as the alphabet. The real mystery here is what ever happened to Walker Lambert's writing ability. His last two books were smoothly written page-turners. The only way you'll want to turn the pages of *The Mystery of Sleepy Lake* is backwards.

2   Coleman Riley fans at least won't be disappointed by their favorite character. This gum-chewing redhead is as absentminded and clumsy as ever. The laughs he provides are almost worth the wooden plot. In one scene, Coleman pops a gum bubble while watching the thieves through a window. The resulting confusion will leave you in stitches. Maybe Walker Lambert is in the wrong line of writing. How about a comedy next time, Walker? That would definitely keep this reviewer awake!

---

4 This passage is an example of a(n)—

Ⓐ review.

Ⓑ biography.

Ⓒ manual.

Ⓓ interview.

5 The author thought the plot of *The Mystery of Sleepy Lake* was—

Ⓐ funny.

Ⓑ confusing.

Ⓒ suspenseful.

Ⓓ boring.

Tired of blurry raindrops sticking to your glasses? Tired of wiping off your spectacles come snow, rain, or fog? Now those days are over, thanks to Wipe-O-Specs. This nifty little gadget clips onto your glasses and works like a pair of miniature windshield wipers. Wipe-O-Specs comes with a convenient battery pack that you can tuck inside a pocket or handbag. When you feel that first drop of rain, simply hook the wire from the battery pack over your ear and snap the wiper blades in place. You'll find the blades to be as light as air and whisper quiet. They even have three speeds! So hurry up and throw out that lint-covered hanky you've been using to wipe off your glasses. Nothing works better than Wipe-O-Specs—and it's only $9.99!

6 The line *Nothing works better than Wipe-O-Specs . . .* tries to persuade the reader to buy a product by—

Ⓐ giving a proven fact about it.

Ⓑ exaggerating how well it works.

Ⓒ explaining how it works.

Ⓓ giving a quote from a satisfied customer.

Example 1 asks you to identify **bias** and different **points of view**. A bias is a strong leaning toward one point of view, or opinion. Many people have a bias toward their own culture. This means they have a strong understanding and good opinion of their own culture, and a weak understanding of other cultures. This may cause them to write or speak unfairly about another culture. It also may cause them to write versions of history that include only information they think is important. Example 1 asks you to think about the events in early America from a point of view that is different from the author's. A good response is supported by examples from the text.

Good: A Wampanoag version would probably say more about the Wampanoag people and less about the colonists. It might talk about the colonists as strangers with strange customs who didn't know how to survive on their own. It might say the Wampanoags felt sorry for the colonists and showed them how to grow food and hunt.

I don't think the Wampanoags would call themselves hostile. They would say the colonists were the invaders because they wanted to take more and more of the Wampanoags' land.

GO ON

A poor response would not answer the question thoroughly and would not use examples from the passage for support.

Poor: A version by a Wampanoag would tell about the same events, but with different words. It would say the Wampanoags were a proud people. It would say the colonists were proud too, but in a different way.

Example 2 asks you to identify an **author's purpose**. Knowing an author's purpose helps you understand a text's meaning as you read. Most texts are written to tell a story, to inform, to instruct, or to persuade. This passage tells events and gives information about the history of the Northeastern region of America. Choice ©, to *inform readers about early American history*, is correct.

Example 3 tests your understanding of **nonfiction**. There are four basic types of literature: nonfiction, fiction, poetry, and drama. The type a writer chooses to use depends on that writer's purpose for writing. All literature types share some of the same **elements**, or characteristics. But each has some elements that make it unique. Fiction, nonfiction, poetry, and drama all may have characters, plots, settings, beginnings, middles, endings, main ideas, and details. But only nonfiction *gives information about real people and real events*. Choice ® is correct.

In **Example 4**, you must identify a **type of nonfiction**. Types of nonfiction include textbooks, encyclopedia articles, newspaper articles, editorials, essays, book or movie reviews, letters, brochures, advertisements, and interviews. Each type of nonfiction has its own **format**, or way of being organized. Although all nonfiction gives information, some nonfiction includes an author's opinions. "Not Walker Lambert's Best Book" is a **book review**. In a review, an author gives information about a movie, book, or performance and also gives an opinion about it. Choice Ⓐ is correct.

Example 5 asks about the **author's view**, or opinion, of the plot of *The Mystery of Sleepy Lake*. In the review he says that the plot *proceeds about as predictably as the alphabet*. This indicates he thinks the plot is *boring*. Choice Ⓓ is correct.

In **Example 6**, you must recognize **persuasive** and **propaganda techniques**. In general, these techniques are used to persuade the reader to do or believe something. The author often makes statements or claims with no supporting evidence. For example, an advertisement might suggest that you buy the new Ridon scooter because "it is the choice of both athletes and celebrities." But the advertisement offers no proof that this statement is true. The last line of the Wipe-O-Specs advertisement tries to persuade readers by *exaggerating how well the product works*. There is no proof to support the author's statement. Choice Ⓑ is correct.

Test-Taking Tips

1 As you read, think about what the author is saying, and why. An author's purpose will affect the text. Is the author trying to tell a story, inform, instruct, or persuade? The purpose will help you begin to decide what type of text you are reading.

2 Think about the author's point of view by noticing what the author has chosen to include in the text. Watch for bias by asking yourself if the author is being fair to all people involved in the events. Is one group of people emphasized? Is one culture described unfairly? Look for words that may be insulting or show a lack of knowledge about other cultures.

3 Look for clues that show an author's beliefs and views. These usually are not stated directly.

4 Read carefully and watch for propaganda and persuasion techniques. These techniques are often appealing because they present false or exaggerated statements as facts. Think about whether an author can support statements he or she makes.

Go for it!

Test Practice 5: Evaluating What You Read   Estimated time: 15 minutes

Directions: Read the passage. Then answer the questions that follow.

Dear Mr. King:

First of all, let me just say that today is your lucky day! As you probably know, Landmass Real Estate is planning a new Sam's Sock Emporium shopping center in your neighborhood. Our company is the leading builder of multilevel sock shops in the world today. Nobody, and I mean nobody, has more experience in socks than we do.

By now, you're probably already excited about the 123 new stores—all devoted to selling fine socks—that will soon be opening near you. But hold on to your own socks, Mr. King; it gets even better. Your house is located on the future site of parking lot C4 of the new Sam's Sock Emporium!

We need your house, Mr. King. In exchange for your house, we are prepared to give you a beautiful, newly redecorated home on Interstate Highway 20—for FREE. That's right, Mr. King, for free! Landmass Real Estate will kindly purchase this property for you.

This house is in a lovely, fast-growing neighborhood, Mr. King. Your new neighbors include Toxico Chemical Refinery on one side and Golden Jim's 24-hour Furniture Warehouse on the other. You will never have another boring, quiet Saturday morning; Golden Jim's brings in crowds of people all day and all night. And talk about a convenient location! Interstate Highway 20 is just 10 feet from your new front door.

Best of all, Mr. King, you will no longer have to live alone. You will even have your very own housemates! That's right—you will be sharing your new home with Mr. and Mrs. Chen, whose home on Elm Street was in the location of future parking lot C6. We are certain you and the Chens will enjoy each other. I'm sure they make delicious Chinese food—all Chinese people do.

On another note, Mr. King, I have had the worst luck trying to contact you. First, I tried telephoning. But as soon as I said the words "Landmass Real Estate," I heard the most horrible screeching sound coming over the wires, and I was forced to hang up.

Next, I tried mailing you a letter, but for some reason, it came back to me a few days later marked "Return to Sender." Even stranger, the envelope was covered with what seemed to be tire tracks.

Next, I tried visiting your house. When I knocked on your door, I was sure I could hear someone inside, but no one ever answered. I guess you must have had your radio on too loud to hear me knock. And then, just as I was walking back to my car, your sprinklers came on and soaked me from head to toe!

So, I'm hoping that my luck has changed and that this letter will make it to you safely. Again, Mr. King, thank you in advance for giving your house to us. There will always be a special place in parking lot C4 saved just for you.

Sincerely,
Ms. Olive Pickering
Landmass Real Estate, Inc.

1 The author wrote this passage mainly to—

Ⓐ inform.

Ⓑ instruct.

Ⓒ persuade.

Ⓓ tell a story.

2 The author used the format of a—

Ⓐ letter.

Ⓑ textbook.

Ⓒ brochure.

Ⓓ interview.

3 When the author says *Nobody, and I mean nobody, has more experience in socks than we do*, she is—

Ⓐ letting Mr. King know that she's giving her opinion.

Ⓑ stating a proven fact.

Ⓒ making a claim without proving it's true.

Ⓓ giving a quote from a satisfied customer.

4 Ms. Pickering seems to believe her company's offer to move Mr. King to a new house is—

Ⓐ kind.

Ⓑ greedy.

Ⓒ insulting.

Ⓓ funny.

5 Which sentence from the passage shows bias?

Ⓐ *We need your house, Mr. King.*

Ⓑ *Interstate Highway 20 is just 10 feet from your new front door.*

Ⓒ *I'm sure they make delicious Chinese food—all Chinese people do.*

Ⓓ *There will always be a special place in parking lot C4 saved just for you.*

GO ON

6 Imagine you are Mr. King. How would he feel about Olive Pickering's reasons for why he should be glad to give up his home? Write a response to Ms. Pickering's letter from Mr. King's point of view. (4 points)

_____

_____

_____

_____

_____

_____

_____

_____

_____

_____

_____

_____

_____

_____

_____

_____

_____

_____

_____

STOP

Points Earned/Total = _____ /9

Comprehension Strategies

This lesson covers . . . using cause and effect and sequence of events to gain meaning and anticipating and constructing meaning from text by making conscious connections to self, an author, and others.

Directions: Read the passage. Then answer the questions that follow.

School Pictures

Rosie quickly changed after morning swim practice. Glimpsing her reflection in the locker room mirror, she let out a groan. "Ugh. Drowned-Ratsville!" She considered drying her hair, but decided against it since she was running a little late.

As Rosie walked the four blocks from the pool to Roosevelt Middle School, her long, wet hair made her shiver. "At least it won't be that long tomorrow," she thought. The string on her little finger was there to remind her to be at the salon at 4 P.M. that afternoon. "Tomorrow's picture will be different!" she vowed. "No more frizz or French braid disasters."

Rosie's last few school pictures had been just awful. One year she had worn two huge pink butterfly barrettes. Another year she had gotten a perm that had made her hair triple in volume. Last year was even worse. Her best friend had tried to give her French braids. Little bunches of hair had stuck out everywhere, making her look like a strange space alien with dozens of short brown antennae.

Rosie had waited a long time for this haircut. She had learned about a program called Locks of Love where you could donate your hair for wigs to be made for children that had lost their hair because of cancer and cancer treatments. Your hair has to be long enough that you can cut off a ten-inch piece. Rosie's hair was finally that long, and she was ready!

Tomorrow's picture was sure to be better. Besides the haircut reminder, Rosie had a rubber band on her wrist so she would remember to ask her sister if she could wear her blue cashmere sweater.

Rosie arrived at her classroom just as the final bell was ringing, but to her surprise, no one was there. She looked down the hall. Suddenly her first period teacher rounded the corner and waved at her. "Hurry up, Rosie! We're all in the cafeteria. Remember? It's picture day!"

www.Photos.com

GO ON

1 What caused Rosie to grow her hair long?

   Ⓐ She kept forgetting about her appointments.

   Ⓑ She had to earn money to pay for a hair cut.

   Ⓒ She had decided to donate hair to Locks of Love.

   Ⓓ She had decided she liked it long.

2 Study the chart. It shows the order of some events in the story.

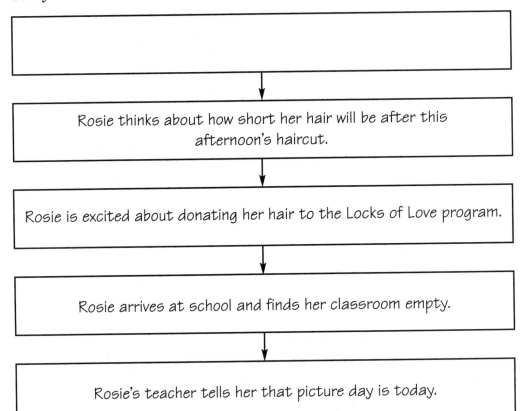

Which event from the story belongs in the empty box?

   Ⓐ Rosie leaves swim practice complaining about her wet, long hair.

   Ⓑ Rosie remembers she wants to borrow her sister's sweater.

   Ⓒ Rosie thinks about her best friend giving her French braids.

   Ⓓ Rosie looks down the hallway to find her classmates.

3 Imagine you are Rosie, many years later, and you find your school picture from that day. What do you think you would remember most about the day: having your picture taken unexpectedly, having 10 inches of your hair cut that afternoon, or donating your hair to Locks of Love? Describe how you would feel about each event. (4 points)

_____

_____

_____

_____

_____

_____

_____

_____

_____

_____

_____

_____

_____

_____

_____

_____

_____

_____

_____

_____

_____

_____

GO ON

In **Example 1**, you must identify a **cause**. A cause is the reason another action takes place. An **effect** is an event that happens because of another event. The story says that Rosie had decided to donate her hair to Locks of Love. It is a program that makes wigs for children who have lost their hair due to cancer treatment. The program requires the hair to be at least 10 inches long. This is what caused her to grow her hair long. Choice ©, *She had decided to donate her hair to Locks of Love*, is correct.

Example 2 asks you to use the **sequence of events** to help you understand the story. Some texts describe many events. A flow chart can help you put the events in order. In this flow chart, the story's first event is missing. *Rosie leaves swim practice complaining about her wet, long hair* is the first event. Choice Ⓐ is correct.

In **Example 3**, you must **make connections** to yourself or others to help you understand the story. Imagining yourself in a similar situation helps you understand a character's actions and predict what the character might do or feel later. A good response describes your feelings about each event.

> **Good:** I would remember donating my hair to cancer patients. I probably wouldn't be happy at all about how I looked in the school picture. Everyone likes to look good in their school picture. But I would get over it. I would probably remember feeling very nervous about having so much hair cut off. But new haircuts sometimes turn out to be exciting too. I would feel the best, however, about donating my hair because I would be helping other kids who might have no hair at all.

A poor response would not give a complete answer.

> **Poor:** I hate getting my hair cut, so I would probably remember that the most. Giving it away would feel good.

Test-Taking Tips

1 For questions about cause and effect, ask yourself these questions: What action or event caused another action to happen? What happened because of another action?

2 When thinking about the sequence, or order, of events, watch for clues such as dates or time of day. These can help you keep the events in order.

3 When asked to write a response that asks what you would do, remember to think about both the passage and yourself. Use your own experiences, opinions and feelings to help you explain what you learned in the passage. Remember to answer each part of the question completely.

Go for it!

Test Practice 6: Comprehension Strategies   Estimated time: 15 minutes

Directions: Read the passage and answer the questions that follow.

Having the Right to Vote

For a long time, women had few rights in this country. They could not own property or keep any money they earned if they were married. And they could not vote. Many women saw the right to vote, called *suffrage*, as crucial, and they struggled for many years to achieve it.

Suffragist Parade in New York City, 1913

Beginnings

Most people point to the year 1848 as the start of the suffrage movement. At that time two determined women, Elizabeth Cady Stanton and Lucretia Mott, called together a meeting at Seneca Falls, New York. The result of the meeting was a document calling for many rights for women, including the right to vote. It was adopted by a slim majority of the attendees. Not long afterward, Stanton became friends with Susan B. Anthony, a strong speaker who could deliver the messages that Stanton wrote. Lucy Stone, another powerful speaker, also became an early "suffragette."

Struggles

In 1870, the Fifteenth amendment was added to the Constitution. Before 1870, the United States Constitution allowed only white men over the age of 21 to vote. The new amendment gave all citizens, including former slaves, the right to vote. However, it did not mention females.

Stanton, Anthony, and others were outraged. They wanted to fight for a new amendment to the U.S. constitution. They thought that all people, including women, should be allowed to vote in national elections. Lucy Stone, however, did not think it was wise to ask for another amendment to the U.S. Constitution right away. She planned instead to convince each state to allow women to vote. And so disagreements developed in the suffragette movement. Some people wanted to work for national voting rights. Others wanted to work for state voting rights.

GO ON

In 1878, Stanton and Anthony's group tried to convince U.S. senators to introduce an amendment giving women national voting rights. The amendment was introduced every year for over forty years, but did not pass.

Success

Throughout those forty years, women were given more opportunities. Several states, especially in the West where there were many frontier women, let women vote in local elections. But they still could not vote for a U.S. president in a national election.

Women became more outspoken in demanding voting rights, and new, younger leaders took over the cause. Protests were held in many cities and even in front of the White House. Some of the women were thrown in jail. But in 1918 President Wilson agreed to support the women's suffrage amendment that was still in the Congress, and it passed. Now all the states needed to ratify, or approve, the amendment. In early 1920 Tennessee, the final state needed to ratify the amendment, voted to support it. And so the Nineteenth Amendment became law.

Elizabeth Cady Stanton and Susan B. Anthony

Photo courtesy of Library of Congress

1 What happened after women held protests at the White House?

Ⓐ Women again disagreed about how to fight for the right to vote.

Ⓑ Former slaves were given the right to vote.

Ⓒ President Wilson agreed to support an amendment, and it passed.

Ⓓ People met in Seneca Falls to make a document about women's rights.

2 The deep division in the suffrage movement was caused by a disagreement over—

Ⓐ whether to hold protests.

Ⓑ whether to work for state or national voting rights.

Ⓒ who should write speeches and who should give them.

Ⓓ who should vote for President Wilson.

3 Study the chart. It shows the order of some events in the passage.

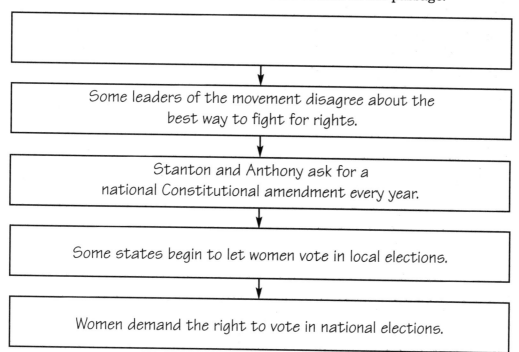

> Some leaders of the movement disagree about the best way to fight for rights.

> Stanton and Anthony ask for a national Constitutional amendment every year.

> Some states begin to let women vote in local elections.

> Women demand the right to vote in national elections.

Which event belongs in the blank box?

Ⓐ Tennessee votes to support the Nineteenth Amendment.
Ⓑ Some women are thrown in jail after protesting at the White House.
Ⓒ Protests were held in many cities.
Ⓓ People meet to make a document saying women should have more rights.

4 Study the diagram.

Cause →	Effect
Tennessee votes to support the Nineteenth Amendment.	

Which statement belongs under "Effect"?

Ⓐ President Wilson supports the Nineteenth Amendment.
Ⓑ Women are thrown in jail for protesting at the White House.
Ⓒ The Nineteenth Amendment is ratified and all U.S. women may vote.
Ⓓ Former slaves receive the right to vote.

5 Suppose you and some of your classmates decide that having the school district choose all the books you read in class is unfair. You think students should have a say in selecting books. You form a group to solve the problem. Explain how your group would accomplish its goal. Based on what you read in the passage, what kind of problems do you think you would have along the way? (4 points)

STOP

Points Earned/Total = _____ /8

Reading Literature

This lesson covers . . . recognizing and understanding themes; distinguishing between major and minor details; and making inferences and providing supporting evidence.

Directions: Read the passage and answer the questions that follow.

The Popular Vote

On her way to turn in her application for fifth-grade class president, Yasmin ran into her friend Samantha Chow. When Sam heard the news, her mouth dropped open. "You mean you're going to run against Mike Diamond?"

Mike Diamond was a shoo-in for class president. Everybody knew it—well, everyone except Yasmin Rao. Mike had served as president in fourth grade. Now he was running again in fifth grade. He was so confident of winning that he wasn't even trying to convince students to vote for him. His ideas were simple: new playground equipment to include a baseball field—to instill school pride, he said. Of course it was no secret that he was captain of the baseball team, but no one really brought that up.

"Excuse me for saying this, Yasmin," blurted Sam, "but you're crazy! You know that Mike's the leader of the popular crowd."

Yasmin shrugged. "The so-called 'popular crowd' only makes up about 20 percent of the class. There are a lot more of us in the 'everybody else crowd.' If I can appeal to the average kid, I think I can win."

Mike didn't view Yasmin as a serious threat, although he did note how every day for two weeks she sat with a different group of people in the lunchroom. "Trying to be Miss Popular," he laughed to his friends. Only on election day did he understand what Yasmin had been doing. She had been listening. Using the information she had gathered, Yasmin had promised to work for the things students were most concerned about. So it wasn't surprising that she won 82 to 28—at least, not to anyone but Mike Diamond.

1 What is the theme of this story?

   Ⓐ Listening to others helps you earn respect.

   Ⓑ Never call someone "crazy."

   Ⓒ Being popular makes running for office easy.

   Ⓓ Never make promises you can't keep.

2 Which detail belongs in a summary of this passage?

   Ⓐ Sam's mouth drops open when she hears that Yasmin will run against Mike Diamond.

   Ⓑ Yasmin shrugs when Sam tells her she's crazy.

   Ⓒ Samantha's last name is Chow.

   Ⓓ Yasmin listened to the concerns of the students.

3 In your own words, explain why Mike Diamond lost the election. Why did the author name the story "The Popular Vote"? Support your answer with examples from the text. (4 points)

_____

_____

_____

_____

_____

_____

_____

_____

_____

_____

_____

    Example 1 asks you to identify the story's **theme**. A theme is a text's central idea or meaning. A theme in a fiction story is often a message the author wants to communicate. Sometimes writers state a theme directly, but more often they do not. To identify a theme that is not stated, you need to think about the story's main message. The message, or main idea, of this story is *Listening to others helps you earn respect*. Choice Ⓐ is correct.

In **Example 2**, you need to tell the difference between **major** and **minor details**. Summaries should include only major details that are necessary to understand the story. Minor details make a story more interesting, but the story still would make sense without them. Choice Ⓓ, *Yasmin listened to the concerns of the students* is an important detail. Choice Ⓓ is correct.

Example 3 asks you to explain why Mike Diamond lost the election. The author does not tell you exactly why, but you can **infer** why he lost. To infer means to make a guess based on evidence in a text. A good answer will support inferences with examples from the text.

Good: Mike Diamond lost the election because he was lazy and selfish. He didn't work to convince students to vote for him. His only idea was one that would benefit himself—a new baseball diamond.

The author named this story "The Popular Vote" because Mike thought that being popular would get him elected. He accused Yasmin of "trying to be Miss Popular" because he thought being popular is all it takes to get elected. It turned out that being "popular" means someone who takes the time to listen to others. Yasmin really was the popular one in the end.

A poor answer wouldn't use evidence from the story for support.

Poor: Mike Diamond didn't win the election because he thought he was popular. He really wasn't, though. He lost to Yasmin in the end because more kids liked her.

Test-Taking Tips

1 When trying to identify a text's theme, think about its central, or main, idea. In fiction, the theme is usually a message, such as *it's best to be honest* or *greed can get you in trouble*. The theme of a nonfiction text is often called its *topic*. It is what the text is mainly about.

2 To help determine whether a detail is major or minor, imagine writing or telling a short summary of the story. Would you include the detail in the summary? If so, it is probably a major detail. If it wouldn't help explain the story, it is a minor detail.

3 To find an inference you must be a detective. You must find clues and gather information from the text. Then you combine the text clues with what you already know. For example, if a story describes people wearing swimsuits and holding towels, you can *infer* that the people are going swimming. Some people call this "reading between the lines." You should always be able to support an inference with evidence from the text.

Go for it!

Test Practice 7: Reading Literature

Estimated time: **15** minutes

Directions: Read the passage and answer the questions that follow.

The Magistrate Settles a Case

A Chinese Folktale

1 A poor farmer was walking along a busy street to take some garbage to the dump. He was carrying old food remains such as smelly cabbage and rotten eggs, so when he accidentally spilled the garbage onto the street, it made a foul-smelling mess.

2 Unfortunately, he spilled the garbage in front of a coat shop whose owner was standing by the door. The merchant, a tall, thin man, looked like a crane hopping around the sidewalk.

3 "What a disgusting pig you are!" said the shop owner to the farmer. "That smell will remain in front of my store for months, and customers will stay away. I think you should pay me for my loss of business!"

4 The farmer gave the merchant his only silver coin, but the merchant still wasn't satisfied. "Take off your coat and use it to wipe up this mess," he told the farmer.

5 "Oh, but I can't," pleaded the farmer. "This is my best coat, the only one that will keep me warm now that winter is here." And he wrapped his good quilted coat tighter around his body.

6 "Very well, then, I will take you to court. I will be satisfied!" said the merchant.

7 Just then the local magistrate came down the street with his assistants. He stopped and asked what the trouble was. Both men told their version of the story.

8 "Very well, then," said the magistrate to the farmer. "Since you admit you are wrong, and since the merchant insists you must wipe up the mess with your coat, then I'm afraid you must. To this merchant, you are a weed in his tidy property."

9 The farmer was too frightened to protest. He removed his quilted coat and cleaned up the garbage. An icy blast blew down the street, and he wrapped his arms around himself.

10 Then the magistrate turned to the shop owner. "We've settled your case, my friend. But now we must settle the farmer's as well."

11 The merchant was astonished. "What do you mean?" he sputtered.

12 "Well," answered the magistrate, "this man is going to freeze out here in the cold, and that is your responsibility. If he should become very ill—or even worse, if he should die—then his family will certainly sue you. You will at the very least lose your store. Are you prepared to face this consequence?"

13 The merchant, needless to say, was now very upset. "What would you have me do?" he asked.

14 "Clearly, you must let this man have a coat from your store," the magistrate replied. "To keep him from suing you,

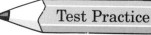

I recommend that you give him the warmest coat you have."

15   The merchant wasn't very happy, but there was nothing he could do but give the farmer an excellent coat. The man bowed his thanks and quickly ran away.

16   "You should be glad I came along," remarked the magistrate to the merchant. "Otherwise, who would have protected your interests from that troublemaker farmer?"

1   Read the following sentence about the farmer from the story.

An icy blast blew down the street, and he wrapped his arms around himself.

You can guess from this sentence that the farmer is—

Ⓐ angry.

Ⓑ happy.

Ⓒ cold.

Ⓓ confused.

2   After the farmer drops the garbage in front of the coat shop, the merchant "looked like a crane hopping around the sidewalk." You can guess that the merchant—

Ⓐ is trying to entertain the farmer.

Ⓑ is trying to avoid stepping in the trash.

Ⓒ does not know the garbage is there.

Ⓓ is trying to kick the garbage away.

3   Which detail does NOT belong in a summary of this story?

Ⓐ The magistrate had assistants.

Ⓑ The merchant wanted to sue the farmer.

Ⓒ The weather was windy and cold.

Ⓓ The magistrate ordered the merchant to give the farmer a coat.

4   A theme in this story is—

Ⓐ Even the poor can get justice.

Ⓑ You can sometimes outsmart the law.

Ⓒ Neatness is important.

Ⓓ It always pays to work hard.

GO ON

5 At the end, the magistrate tells the merchant he has protected him from the "troublemaker" farmer. Do you think the magistrate really thinks the farmer is a troublemaker? Use evidence from the story to support your answer. (4 points)

_____

_____

_____

_____

_____

_____

_____

_____

_____

_____

_____

_____

_____

_____

_____

_____

_____

_____

_____

STOP

Points Earned/Total = _____ /8

Literary Elements

This lesson covers . . . identifying genre and recognizing literary elements in stories, including setting, characters, plot, and mood.

Directions: Read the passage and answer the questions that follow.

All for a Little Food and Drink

1   As the hot California sun rose, Mesquite John woke up with a powerful hunger. He looked all around for something to eat, but the usual six dozen eggs and side of bacon for breakfast just didn't seem to be enough today. As he sat thinking about what to do, he heard a loud popping sound from nearby. Mesquite John walked over to investigate and discovered that the blazing sun was popping an entire cornfield. He quickly sprinkled a tub of butter and a bag of salt on an acre of popcorn and dove into his breakfast. Everything was going fine until Mesquite John started getting thirsty. In fact, his throat felt so dry that he began to cough. He coughed so hard that pretty soon he created a tremendous windstorm.

2   Mesquite John coughed his way across two states in search of water. When he reached the Great Salt Lake, he filled three huge buckets with salt water and quickly gulped them down. By the time he realized his mistake, Mesquite John was ten times thirstier than he was before. In his anger, he kicked the ground and made the Rocky Mountains get even higher. He leaped over the mountains in one big jump and headed for the Great Lakes. Mesquite John drank so much of that fresh, sweet water that the lakes were dry for a week.

www.Photos.com

GO ON

1 This passage is an example of a—

    Ⓐ fantasy.

    Ⓑ tall tale.

    Ⓒ myth.

    Ⓓ fable.

2 Mesquite John crosses the Rocky Mountains and goes to the Great Lakes because—

    Ⓐ salt water has made him very thirsty.

    Ⓑ he gets angry while visiting the Great Salt Lake.

    Ⓒ it is easy for him to jump over mountains.

    Ⓓ he wants to see different scenery.

Example 1 asks you to identify the story's **genre**, or type. Each genre has its own characteristics. This story is a *tall tale*. Its main character is an imaginary person whose size and actions are exaggerated and humorous. Choice Ⓑ is correct.

The chart explains the characteristics of some types of literature.

Genre	Characteristics
fantasy	unreal characters and setting
myth	often about gods and goddesses; may tell how something in nature came to be
tall tale	about an imaginary and larger-than-life person, uses humor and exaggeration; usually takes place in the American West in the 1800s
realistic fiction	realistic characters, setting, and situation
historical fiction	characters are either imaginary or based on real historical figures; takes place in the past
science fiction	imaginary characters; takes place in the future

Example 2 asks about the story's **plot**. The events that occur in the story make up the plot. Most plots start with a main problem that characters try to solve. In this story, Mesquite John's main problem is that he is hungry and then thirsty. Every event is an attempt to solve this main problem. When more problems occur along the way, the plot "thickens," or becomes more complicated. As John finds food, he then needs water. But when he discovers that water from the Great *Salt* Lake is salty, he heads for some fresh water in the Great Lakes. He does this because *salt water has made him very thirsty*. Choice Ⓐ is correct.

Linnie's Letters

1   Elinore's family had decided to move west. They had heard lots of wonderful stories about life out west. People said that it had rich farmland, growing towns, and even gold. The family all agreed. Papa, Mama, and Elinore would ride in one wagon. Elinore's sister Phoebe would ride in another wagon with her husband Robert.

2   But the trip had not been easy. Almost from the beginning, Phoebe and her husband Robert had troubles. Their wagon nearly tipped over at a river crossing. One of their oxen broke a leg, and they ruined two wagon wheels. Their wagon was simply too heavy for the journey.

3   "You've got to lighten your load," the train leader ordered. "That piano is your problem."

4   Robert refused to leave the piano. He was as stubborn as a mule. The wagon train leader said that they would leave him behind.

5   "Let them go," Phoebe said. "Our family will travel on its own."

6   "No," said Papa firmly. "We should not try to cross this trail on our own. That would be foolish. The only answer is to lighten your load."

7   Robert took Phoebe by the hand. "Come, dear," he said quietly. "Help me stand our wagon upright."

8   Mama reached out and stopped Robert. "What do you plan to do?"

9   "We'll go back to the prairie town we just passed and make our home there," Robert replied as he turned and headed back to his wagon.

10   "But Robert," Mama said softly. "It's only a piano. Just leave it here and come with us."

11   "It is not only a piano," Robert said shortly.

12   Elinore watched as Robert led her dear sister Phoebe away. Three men from the wagon train helped them straighten their wagon. Within minutes, the wagon train continued its journey west. Elinore walked slowly behind her parents' covered wagon.

13   Up ahead, Mama and Papa faced forward, stubbornly, as they all moved up the steep hill, away from Robert and Phoebe.

14   Only Elinore looked back. <u>Tears</u> filled her brown eyes. She watched as Robert and her only sister turned and rode off in the opposite direction. Would she ever see her sister again?

3 If Elinore has the chance to see Phoebe again, she will most likely—

Ⓐ ignore her.

Ⓑ be polite.

Ⓒ yell at her.

Ⓓ welcome her.

4 What is the mood of the story?

Ⓐ cheerful

Ⓑ tense

Ⓒ mysterious

Ⓓ humorous

5 Where and when does this story take place? Explain how you know. Do you think this plot would make sense in present time? Explain why or why not. (4 points)

_____

_____

_____

_____

_____

_____

_____

_____

_____

Example 3 asks you about the **character** Elinore. Questions about characters may ask what kind of person a character is, how a character feels about something, or why a character does something in the story. They might also ask how characters are alike or different, how they deal with other characters, or what changes they undergo in a story. You must decide what Elinore will do next based on what you know about her already. The author describes Phoebe as Elinore's "dear" sister. Elinore also cries as she looks back at her sister in the end. These clues show that Elinore would most likely *welcome her* when she sees her again. Choice Ⓓ is correct.

In **Example 4**, you must choose the best description of the **mood** of the passage. The mood is the feeling the reader gets while reading a passage. The author tries to use words and action to create this mood. This story describes a serious family conflict. The characters' feelings and actions cause the family to split apart. The author uses the words *stubbornly* and *shortly* to help show the characters' anger and tension. The best description of the mood is *tense*, choice ⑧.

Example 5 asks about the story's **setting**. The setting is the time and place during which the events of the story take place. The setting often contributes to the main problem, or conflict, in the story. It may also affect how the problem is solved. A good response uses examples from the story.

> **Good:** The setting is probably in the 1800s because that is when people used covered wagons to move west. It takes place in a prairie. We know this because Robert says they just passed a prairie town.
>
> People now do not try to travel in covered wagons, especially with a piano. Now there are good roads and vehicles for moving heavy things. So this situation probably would not exist today. Families might split up for some reasons, but not because a piano is too heavy for their wagon.

A poor response would not use examples from the story.

> **Poor:** The story takes place in the 1800s. Wagons do not exist anymore, so the story wouldn't make sense now.

Test-Taking Tips

1 To answer questions about **plot**, think about how the story begins, what happens in the middle, and how it ends. Try to determine the main problem and how one event leads to another until the problem is solved.

2 To answer questions about a **character** in the story, look at the details. How the character looks and what the character thinks, does, and says are all clues.

3 To answer questions about **setting**, see if the story tells you where the action is taking place. If the story doesn't say specifically, look for clues that could help you figure it out. Are characters inside or outside? Do characters use objects that existed only in a certain time period? What surroundings does the narrator describe?

4 To help describe a story's **mood**, think about how you felt when you read it.

Go for it!

Test Practice 8: Literary Elements

Estimated time: **20** minutes

Directions: Read the passage. Then answer the questions that follow.

Perry Moves In

Perry stepped into the elevator with his arms full of boxes. He tried to whistle, but the lump in his throat was in his way.

"So, you are new in this apartment building?" the elevator man asked.

Perry blinked back a tear and nodded.

"I, too, moved when I was your age," the man said in heavily accented English. "Imagine, I had never been outside the village before. I had never even seen car. Suddenly I am in land of buildings like . . . like mountains. I almost—"

The elevator doors slid open at the 26th floor. "This is your floor, yes?" the man said, gallantly helping Perry out.

Perry walked down the hall, wondering about the man. What was his name? What country was he from? And what was he about to say when the elevator doors opened? Perry thought about the old man as he unpacked. He was eager to ride the elevator again.

"As I say, I almost jumped off the boat and swam back to the village," the man continued when Perry entered the elevator a second time. "I feel I cannot live in the city of smoke and noise."

Perry smiled. He knew about those kinds of feelings.

"So rude—I have not told you my name!" the man exclaimed. "I am Aldo, but the friends call me Al." Al solemnly exchanged introductions with Perry, then continued talking until the elevator door opened. From then on, Al told more about his life every time Perry stepped in the elevator. He talked about coming from Italy to help his father run a fruit-and-vegetable stand. He was such a good storyteller that sometimes Perry rode up and down just to hear more.

One day Perry brought a new friend home from school. Al smiled as the boys chatted and laughed together in the elevator. When Perry stepped into the elevator the next morning, Al asked, "You and your friend have fun, yes?"

"We had a great time," Perry answered. "But I want to hear more of your stories."

"No more stories to tell," Al said.

"Sure there are," Perry insisted. "I never learned what happened after the horse ate your father's apples."

Al put his hand on Perry's shoulder. "You have been kind to hear this old man talk. I saw you were lonely, and I tell myself, even foolish stories are better than sad heart. Now you have friends. You are happy. You don't need these stories anymore."

"I may not *need* to hear them, but I want to hear them—more than you can know," Perry said softly.

© *Perfection Learning*® **No reproduction permitted.**

1 This story takes place—

Ⓐ in a department store.

Ⓑ in a city apartment building.

Ⓒ somewhere in Italy.

Ⓓ in a big house in the country.

2 How does Perry feel about being in a new place?

Ⓐ excited   Ⓒ bored

Ⓑ angry   Ⓓ sad

3 Al tells Perry stories in order to—

Ⓐ cure his fear of elevators.

Ⓑ teach him a lesson.

Ⓒ convince him to visit Italy.

Ⓓ make him feel better.

4 Al stops telling stories when Perry—

Ⓐ starts school.

Ⓑ brings a friend to visit.

Ⓒ moves to a new apartment.

Ⓓ asks about his father.

5 Which word best describes the mood at the end of the story?

Ⓐ happy   Ⓒ sad

Ⓑ humorous   Ⓓ suspenseful

6 Al is the kind of person who—

Ⓐ cares about others' feelings.

Ⓑ gets upset easily.

Ⓒ thinks mostly about himself.

Ⓓ always wants to have fun.

Directions: Read the passage and answer the questions that follow.

Proserpine

After the earth was created, Pluto was assigned to be the god of the Underworld. Usually he stayed in his dark home, but one day he was walking about the earth's surface. In a beautiful garden he saw the young maiden Proserpine gathering flowers. Pluto instantly fell in love with her. He quickly put her in his chariot and carried her off, against her wishes, to his Underworld home.

Now Proserpine was the daughter of Ceres, the goddess of farms and the harvest. It was she who kept the crops and flowers growing all year. When she realized that her daughter was missing, she became very sad. She searched through the whole world but could not find Proserpine. In her grief she blamed the earth. She made the farm animals die and the crops stop growing. Soon the earth was dry and miserable. People were starving.

After many months, Ceres met a woodland nymph who knew what had happened to Proserpine. After she heard the nymph's story, she went to Jupiter, the chief god, and begged him to help her get her daughter back. Jupiter agreed, with one condition. Proserpine must not have eaten anything while she was in the Underworld.

Ceres entered the Underworld and demanded that Pluto release her daughter. While Proserpine was in the Underworld, though, she had eaten one tiny seed. So she could not go back to earth forever. Jupiter did agree, though, that she could spend one half of each year there, with her mother.

When Proserpine returned to earth, Ceres was joyful and let all the plants begin to grow again. But every year when her daughter leaves her, the earth gets dry and empty.

GO ON

7 This story is an example of—

Ⓐ a myth.

Ⓑ realistic fiction.

Ⓒ historical fiction.

Ⓓ a tall tale.

8 What is the main problem in this story? Explain how it is solved. Also tell what this story explains about nature. (4 points)

_____

_____

_____

_____

_____

_____

_____

_____

_____

_____

_____

_____

_____

_____

_____

_____

_____

_____

STOP

Points Earned/Total = _____ /11

Literary Devices and Structures

This lesson covers . . . identifying and responding to the elements of sound and structure in poetry; recognizing figurative language in text, such as simile, metaphor, personification, and alliteration; interpreting idiomatic expressions; and identifying the structure of drama.

Directions: Read the poem and answer the questions that follow.

From a Railway Carriage
by Robert Louis Stevenson

www.Photos.com

Faster than fairies, faster than witches,
Bridges and houses, hedges and ditches;
And charging along like troops in a battle,
All through the meadows the horses and cattle:
All of the sights of the hill and the plain
Fly as thick as driving rain;
And ever again, in the wink of an eye,
Painted stations whistle by.

Here is a child who clambers and scrambles,
All by himself and gathering brambles;
Here is a tramp who stands and gazes;
And there is the green for stringing the daisies!
Here is a cart run away in the road
Lumping along with man and load;
And here is a mill and there is a river:
Each a glimpse and gone for ever!

1 In this poem, the author uses words that create a rhythm, or beat. This poem's rhythm is—

Ⓐ gentle, like daisies blowing in the breeze.

Ⓑ smooth and soaring, like a flying fairy or witch.

Ⓒ slow and lazy, like cattle grazing.

Ⓓ rapid and regular, like a train on tracks.

2 Which phrase best describes how the author organized this poem?

    Ⓐ into one stanza, with no pattern to the rhyme

    Ⓑ into two stanzas, with a pattern of two rhyming lines in a row

    Ⓒ into two stanzas, in which every other line rhymes

    Ⓓ into sixteen stanzas, with three rhyming lines in a row

3 What does the author mean when he says the sights he sees from the train "fly as thick as driving rain"?

    Ⓐ All the sights have wings.

    Ⓑ The sights pass by slowly.

    Ⓒ The sights pass by quickly.

    Ⓓ All the sights are wet with rain.

Directions: Read the poem and answer the questions that follow.

The crimson sun sinks slowly to the brink
Of the shimmering, wave-tossed sea.
Old friends, they meet again
Greeting evening more gently than morning.
Like the sea, the sun has its rhythms —
Rising and falling, rising and falling —
A slow-motion dancer moving through the sky
Gliding toward its moment of glory
When it merges with the waiting sea.
Too soon the moment is over:
The sea is darkening,
The sun bows out.
For unlike the sea,
The sun cannot dance forever.

4 In the poem, the sun is compared to—

    Ⓐ the sky.   Ⓒ a wave.

    Ⓑ a dancer.   Ⓓ darkness.

5 Which line shows the repetition of the same beginning consonant sound?

    Ⓐ *The crimson sun sinks slowly to the brink*

    Ⓑ *Of the shimmering, wave-tossed sea.*

    Ⓒ *A slow-motion dancer moving through the sky*

    Ⓓ *Gliding toward its moment of glory*

In **Example 1**, you must describe the **sound** the poem makes as you read it. All poems have a beat, or a rhythm, to them. Poets, like musicians, choose rhythms to express a certain feeling, idea, or experience. In this poem the author tries to give the reader the feeling of riding on the train. The alternating two- and one-syllable words create a rhythm that is *rapid and regular, like a train on tracks*. Choice Ⓓ is correct.

Example 2 asks about the poem's **structure**. This poem is organized into two groups, or stanzas. Each stanza has eight lines. The poem also has a regular, AABB rhyming pattern. This means that the first two lines rhyme with each other, the next two lines rhyme with each other, and so on. This pattern is repeated throughout the poem. The best description of this poem's structure is choice Ⓑ, *into two stanzas, with a pattern of two rhyming lines in a row*.

In **Example 3**, you must explain the meaning of a **simile**. Writers often create comparisons to help their readers see things in new ways. A simile is one kind of comparison in which a writer compares two things that seem to be different. The comparison is shown with the word *like* or *as*. In the poem, the speed of the sights is compared to driving rain. Since driving rain falls with great speed, the writer means *the sights pass by quickly*. Choice Ⓒ is correct.

A **metaphor** is another type of comparison. It also compares two things that seem to be different. But it does not use the words *like* or *as*. One thing is said to *be* another. If the author had used a metaphor to describe the speed of the sights passing by, he would have written that the sights *are* driving rain.

Example 4 asks about another way authors help readers see things in new ways. In this poem, the author uses **personification** to help describe the sun. Personification is when a nonhuman thing is described as if it were human. In one line of this poem the sun is described as a *slow-motion dancer moving through the sky*. Another line says the *sun bows out*, as if from a dance. Finally, the last line says the sun *cannot dance forever*. Throughout the poem, the author describes the sun as if it is a human *dancer*. Choice Ⓑ is correct.

In **Example 5**, you must identify an example of **alliteration**. Poets often choose words for the beauty of their sound as well as for their meaning. Alliteration is when two or more words with the same initial sound are placed next to one another. The author of this poem uses alliteration in the first line, *The crimson sun sinks slowly to the brink*. Choice Ⓐ is correct.

An **idiomatic expression** is another type of description. It is an expression whose meaning is different from the ordinary meaning of the words in it. Each culture and language has its own idioms. If your brother says "This class is over my head," he doesn't mean that the class is taking place above his head. He means that he doesn't understand the lessons.

The chart defines and gives examples of **literary devices**.

Literary Device	Definition	Example
simile	a comparison of two unlike things using the word *like* or *as*	Her smile was like sunshine.
metaphor	a comparison of two unlike things without using *like* or *as*	His heart was a beating drum.
personification	giving a nonhuman thing human characteristics	The fog crept through the village.
alliteration	when two or more nearby words have the same initial sound	a misty, moist morning a bleak and bitter night
idiomatic expression	expression has a meaning different from the ordinary meaning of the words in it	pull my leg (joke with me) hit it off (get along)

Directions: Read this excerpt from a play. Then answer the questions that follow.

from **The New Kid**

ACT I, Scene 2
A park on a summer afternoon. TRAN is walking through the park trying to find kids who will play with him. He spots TONY, who is tossing pebbles into a pond. TRAN at first hides behind a tree, then approaches TONY.

TRAN *(takes a deep breath)*: Hey! I'm Tran.

TONY *(looks up suddenly)*: Hi. My name's Tony—I'm the new kid.

TRAN: Are you serious? I thought I was the new kid. We moved to town last week.

TONY: I moved here from Minnesota about a month ago. I guess that means I'm not the new kid anymore—at least not the newest kid.

TRAN: Do you like basketball? Want to go to my house and shoot some hoops?

6 The scene *before* this one would be called—

    Ⓐ ACT I.

    Ⓑ ACT I, Scene 1.

    Ⓒ Scene 3.

    Ⓓ ACT 0, Scene 1.

7 The purpose of the stage directions is to—

    Ⓐ show what the actors will say.

    Ⓑ describe the setting and the actors' actions.

    Ⓒ show what a narrator will say.

    Ⓓ give the audience something to read.

    Example 6 tests your understanding of the **structure of drama**. Dramas, or plays, are generally broken into separate acts or scenes and contain several characters. Most plays have two acts. Each act is usually divided into two or more scenes. Since this part of the play is from *ACT I, Scene 2*, the scene before this would be called *ACT I, Scene 1*. Choice Ⓑ is correct.

    Example 7 asks about the purpose of stage directions. Dramas are intended to be performed for an audience. The story is told through the characters' actions and the things they say to each other. A written version of a play is called a *script*. It includes all the actors' spoken parts. It also includes stage directions. These *describe the setting and the actors' actions*. Choice Ⓑ is correct.

Test-Taking Tips

1 Remember that sound is as important in poetry as meaning. Pay close attention to the rhythms and sounds in a poem and try to figure out what the author is expressing with them.

2 Not all poems are broken into stanzas, and not all have a regular rhyming pattern. Some don't rhyme at all. All poems, however, express a feeling, idea, or situation; are written in lines; and have some kind of rhythm.

3 Figurative language—similes, metaphors, personification, and alliteration—is found in all types of literature, not just in poetry. Idiomatic expressions are often used in everyday speech.

Go for it!

Test Practice 9:
Literary Devices and Structures

Estimated time: **15** minutes

Directions: Read the passage and answer the questions that follow.

A Sense of Balance

1   Ruby had butterflies in her stomach as she waited her turn at the balance beam. She looked wistfully over at the uneven bars. Why couldn't she take an extra turn on those instead? She felt as light as a bird when she swung on the uneven bars; dismounting was like flying. Even a turn on the trampoline or the horse would be better than the balance beam—at least she wouldn't look foolish.

2   "You're up," Ms. Greenberg called out to Ruby. "Nina and Beth will be your spotters."

3   Ruby rubbed chalk dust on her bare feet. She didn't want to take any chances on slipping. Then she climbed onto the balance beam and tried to stand up. Her knees were soft pudding; her heart pounded. "You can do it," she whispered to herself. She took a tiny step forward, and suddenly the world shifted sideways. Nina and Beth reached out to steady her as she staggered.

4   "You're doing fine," Ms. Greenberg said reassuringly. "Try again."

5   Ruby gritted her teeth and took a second step. This time the world turned upside down. She crashed off the beam before Nina and Beth had time to react. Ruby stood up and quickly dusted herself off.

1   In paragraph 1, Ruby had "butterflies in her stomach" as she waited to use the balance beam. This means she—

Ⓐ had swallowed some butterflies.

Ⓑ felt as light as a butterfly.

Ⓒ felt very happy.

Ⓓ was very nervous.

2   When Ruby thinks about the uneven bars in paragraph 1, she compares herself to a—

Ⓐ bird.   Ⓒ foolish person.

Ⓑ horse.   Ⓓ butterfly.

3   In paragraph 3, as Ruby first stands up on the beam, her knees—

Ⓐ turn into real pudding.

Ⓑ feel weak and soft, like pudding.

Ⓒ have pudding on them.

Ⓓ look like pudding.

Directions: Read the passage and answer the questions that follow.

from **Paul Revere's Ride**

by Henry Wadsworth Longfellow

This passage is from a long poem about the famous journey of Paul Revere during the Revolutionary War. On April 18, 1775, he rode on horseback all through the night from Boston toward Concord. His mission was to warn American colonists of the arrival of British troops.

It was one by the village clock,
When he galloped into Lexington.
He saw the gilded weathercock
Swim in the moonlight as he passed,
And the meeting-house windows,
  blank and bare
Gaze at him with a spectral[1] glare,
As if they already stood aghast
At the bloody work they would look upon.

It was two by the village clock,
When he came to the bridge in
  Concord town.
He heard the bleating of the flock,
And the twitter of the birds among
  the trees,
And felt the breath of the morning breeze
Blowing over the meadows brown.
And one was safe and asleep in his bed
Who at the bridge would be first to fall,
Who at the bridge would be lying dead,
Pierced by a British musket-ball.

[1] **spectral** ghostly

4 This passage shows two complete stanzas from the poem. Which phrase best describes how the poem is organized?

Ⓐ into stanzas of different lengths and different rhyming patterns

Ⓑ into stanzas of different lengths, with no rhyming words

Ⓒ into stanzas of the same length, in which every other line rhymes

Ⓓ into stanzas of the same length, in which every two lines rhyme

5 The first three lines of each stanza are very similar. They begin the same way and have similar rhythms and rhymes. This gives the feeling of—

Ⓐ moonlight shining on houses.

Ⓑ birds chirping in the trees.

Ⓒ a gentle morning breeze.

Ⓓ a horse galloping on and on.

6 Which of the following lines contains an example of alliteration?

Ⓐ *Swim in the moonlight as he passed*

Ⓑ *And the meeting-house windows, blank and bare*

Ⓒ *He heard the bleating of the flock*

Ⓓ *And the twitter of the birds among the trees*

7 What is meant by "And felt the breath of the morning breeze"?

Ⓐ The morning has turned into a person who can breathe.

Ⓑ The wind has turned into a person who is breathing on Paul Revere.

Ⓒ Paul Revere can feel the morning approaching.

Ⓓ There is a strong breeze.

GO ON

Directions: Read the passage and answer the questions that follow.

A Ride in April

Cast of Characters

Minutemen:
Paul Revere
Sam Johnson
Jeb Green

British:
General Thomas Gage
Private Deering

ACT I, Scene 1

It is late on an April night in 1775. Two men, dressed in homespun shirts and britches, are standing outside the North Church. The stage is fairly dark, bathed in a deep blue light. There are weak spotlights on the two men, and the outline of the North Church tower is visible in the background. The bell in the tower is even more weakly lighted. The two men are talking quietly and looking around nervously as they speak.

PAUL: The British are on the move tonight, Sam—I can feel it in my bones. I fear they're after the guns we've stored down in Concord.

SAM: If they get those weapons we'll all be doomed. How can we hold off the British without arms? Our cause—the cause of liberty—depends on our taking some action.

PAUL: It's good that the minutemen have worked out a plan for situations like this. First we need to find out if the British are moving down on land or by sea. Once we get the signal, we can ride and warn all the patriots in the area.

---

8 Which of the following is a stage direction?

Ⓐ *It is late on an April night in 1775.*

Ⓑ *The British are on the move tonight, Sam—I can feel it in my bones.*

Ⓒ *I fear they're after the guns we've stored down in Concord.*

Ⓓ *Once we get the signal, we can ride and warn all the patriots in the area.*

9 The next scene will be called—

Ⓐ ACT II.

Ⓑ Scene 3.

Ⓒ ACT II, Scene 2.

Ⓓ ACT I, Scene 2.

STOP

Points Earned/Total = _____ /9

Mastery Test   Estimated time: **60** minutes

Directions: Read the passage and answer the questions that follow.

Paul Bunyan

Lumberjacks were <u>big</u>, strong men. But Paul Bunyan was the biggest and strongest of all. He was so big that he used a pine tree to comb his beard. He was so strong that he could drive a tree stump into the ground with his fist.

Of course, Paul was a lot smaller when he was a baby in Maine. But he was still bigger than any baby was supposed to be. In fact, some folks say that baby Paul's size got him thrown out of the state. It seems that baby Paul knocked down miles of trees every time he rolled over. Everyone wanted Paul out of Maine before he did some serious damage.

No one knows exactly where Paul and his family went next. But we do know that Paul showed up years later in Wisconsin. Or it might have been Minnesota. In those days, some states were completely covered with dark green forests. They were beautiful all right, but pioneers needed those trees to build houses, barns, wagons, bridges, and boats. So Paul decided to become a lumberjack.

Naturally, Paul was no ordinary lumberjack. There was the time that he dug a river. This happened in Minnesota for sure. Paul was cutting trees there, and he had to move them all the way to New Orleans. The easiest way to do that would be to float the logs south. But there was no river that went from Minnesota to New Orleans.

So Paul did some thinking. While he thought, he ate a snack. Nothing much. Just 3 hams, 10 loaves of bread, 150 pancakes, and 5 gallons of cider. But that gave Paul enough strength to dig. He dug the river that very afternoon. All the way from Minnesota to New Orleans. He called it the <u>Mississippi</u>.

As you can imagine, Paul's logging camps were big. The dining hall was so long that you couldn't see from one end to another. And the food? Well, it took a lot of food to feed Paul and his crew. That's why Paul's blacksmith made a huge iron pot that held 1000 gallons of soup. The thing was so big that the cook had to use a rowboat when he made soup. He'd row out into the middle and dump in potatoes, cabbage, and meat.

Paul had himself a special friend too. He found his friend one cold winter while out for a walk. He hadn't gone far when he tripped over something in the snow. Well, Paul wondered what was there. After all, it had to be pretty big to trip him up. So he started digging through the snow. Before long he uncovered an ox—a blue ox!

It was easy to see that the ox was a baby. Still, it was half as big as Paul. So Paul carried the poor thing back to camp and named it Babe.

Babe kept on growing. He got so heavy that he left footprints in solid

GO ON

rock. But Babe's size came in handy. It didn't take Paul and his crew long to chop down all the trees in an area. Then they'd have to move on. But they didn't have to build a new logging camp. Paul would just hitch the buildings to Babe. Then the big blue ox would drag everything along with him.

They cleared a lot of land that way too.

Then there was the time in Wisconsin where the road between the camp and the forest was very twisty. It was so twisty that men going to work met themselves coming back! It took the men far too long to get to work on such a twisty road. But Paul always had <u>a trick up his sleeve</u>. He hitched Babe up to one end of the road and then gave him a couple of tugs. He huffed and puffed once or twice. Then *ping*! That road snapped like a rubber band. Then it lay down nice and straight like a road should.

No one knows what happened to Paul and Babe. Some say they finished their work. Then they went into the woods to take a nap.

It could be that they're still there.

1 In the beginning, the story is set in—

Ⓐ Maine.

Ⓑ Wisconsin.

Ⓒ Mississippi.

Ⓓ Minnesota.

2 Paul decided to become a lumberjack because—

Ⓐ he loved being in the woods.

Ⓑ his parents owned a logging company.

Ⓒ he made a good living as a lumberjack.

Ⓓ the country needed wood for building things.

3 What caused Paul to create the Mississippi River?

Ⓐ He needed drinking water.

Ⓑ He needed to travel south for the winter.

Ⓒ He needed to float logs down to New Orleans.

Ⓓ Other rivers weren't deep enough.

4 The mood of this passage is—

Ⓐ tense.

Ⓑ sad.

Ⓒ mysterious.

Ⓓ humorous.

5 How many syllables are in the word <u>Mississippi</u>?

Ⓐ three

Ⓑ four

Ⓒ five

Ⓓ six

6 Read the thesaurus entry for <u>big</u>.

> **BIG**
>
> *adjective*
>
> **enormous** — Extremely large. *Dinosaurs were enormous creatures.*
>
> **important** — Significant or major. *The president is an important person.*
>
> **older** — Grown-up. *My grandparents are older.*
>
> **spacious** — Having a large space. *The rooms in the castle were spacious.*

Which word is the best replacement for <u>big</u> in the first paragraph?

Ⓐ enormous

Ⓑ important

Ⓒ older

Ⓓ spacious

7 According to the story, when a road was too twisty for the loggers, Paul had <u>a trick up his sleeve</u>. This means that he—

Ⓐ liked to do magic tricks.

Ⓑ wasn't good at keeping secrets.

Ⓒ always wore long-sleeved shirts.

Ⓓ had a clever idea.

8 The story's theme is—

Ⓐ huge jobs require huge effort.

Ⓑ it's lots of fun to be a lumberjack.

Ⓒ large people have good hearts.

Ⓓ logging can be dangerous.

GO ON

9 Explain why this story is a tall tale. Use three examples from the passage to support your answer. (4 points)

_____

_____

_____

_____

_____

_____

_____

_____

_____

_____

_____

_____

_____

_____

_____

_____

_____

_____

_____

_____

Directions: Read the passage and answer the questions that follow.

from Almost Sisters

ACT I, Scene 2

It is an early spring evening in Gettysburg, Pennsylvania, during the Civil War. SALLIE RANDALL sits across the kitchen table from MA.

MA: What do you think, Sallie?

(SALLIE stares at her mother with a look of disbelief.)

MA: It seems your dear pa—may he rest in peace—had a lot of debt. He gave many supplies to the army. I'm not upset; this war is a good cause. But now that he's gone, well, we are as poor as church mice. There is just no other solution.

SALLIE: We could live with Aunt Clara and Uncle Will.

MA: Yes, we could. But I do not want to stay in Gettysburg. There are just too many memories of that <u>horrible</u> battle. Besides, I want us to make a new start together—you and me, Sallie.

SALLIE: But what about my friends, and Aunt Clara, and Uncle Will?

MA: We'll meet new people, make new friends. You know we will. I sold the store to pay off our debt and have a small sum left to start our new life. I've been reading about the Homestead Act. It says that 160 acres of land is available to the head of any household. *(MA sits up straight and points to herself.)* That's me. If we live there for five years and improve the land, it will be ours, for free. We can raise crops and animals, Sallie. We can provide for ourselves.

SALLIE: But Ma! We don't know how to farm!

MA: That is why I have arranged to work at a neighbor's farm in Kansas. He is a widower with a son and daughter around your age. I will keep house for them and he will teach us how to work our land. Our land, Sallie. *(MA reaches across the table to take Sallie's hands. She speaks softly now.)* Can I count on you? Shall we step out in faith and start a new life together?

SALLIE: *(Thinks for a few moments, then smiles.)* Yes, Ma. You can count on me.

10 The scene *before* this one in the play is—

Ⓐ Scene 3.

Ⓑ ACT I, Scene 1.

Ⓒ ACT I.

Ⓓ ACT II, Scene 1.

11 When Ma says "may he rest in peace," and talks about the war and a battle, you can guess that Pa—

Ⓐ is resting in another room.

Ⓑ will join them in Kansas later.

Ⓒ was probably killed in the war.

Ⓓ has been kidnapped.

12 What best helps you understand that Ma feels proud to be the head of the household?

Ⓐ Ma's line: *But I do not want to stay in Gettysburg.*

Ⓑ Sallie's line: *But Ma! We don't know how to farm!*

Ⓒ The stage direction: *MA sits up straight and points to herself.*

Ⓓ Ma's line: *He is a widower with a son and daughter around your age.*

13 What problem will need to be solved in the rest of the play?

Ⓐ Aunt Clara and Uncle Will don't want to go to Kansas.

Ⓑ Sallie is uneasy about leaving her friends and moving to a new home.

Ⓒ Ma can't convince Sallie to move to Kansas.

Ⓓ Sallie can't convince Ma to stay in Gettysburg.

14 Which word means the OPPOSITE of horrible?

Ⓐ shocking

Ⓑ little

Ⓒ simple

Ⓓ wonderful

15 If this were a fiction story instead of a play, how would it be different? Explain what elements of a play you wouldn't need in a fiction story. Use examples from the story to explain your answer. (4 points)

_____

_____

_____

_____

_____

_____

_____

_____

_____

_____

_____

_____

_____

_____

_____

_____

_____

_____

_____

_____

Directions: Read the passage and answer the questions that follow.

MONDAY   COASTAL NEWS   FEBRUARY 20

Busy Season for Marine Animal Rescuers

Workers at the Marine Mammal Stranding Center (MMSC) in Brigantine, New Jersey, could use a break. They have found an unusually high number of seals on shores this year. The center staff is working long hours to help all the animals and return them safely to the ocean.

MMSC rescues <u>stranded</u> whales, dolphins, seals, and sea turtles that have washed ashore on New Jersey beaches. These animals range from 5-pound sea turtles to 25-ton humpback whales. Most stranded animals suffer from injury or illness. Shark bites are common, as well as illness from parasites and disease.

Human activity also harms some marine animals. The animals eat plastic trash and become tangled in fishing nets. Large boats can strike them, and toxic pollution can make them very ill.

Most of the seal pups found this year are about two to three weeks old. This is just the age when their mothers leave them. Many pups are able to use instinct to survive by then. Others, however, take a little longer.

A very young female gray seal was the first to appear this year. On January 24 workers found her covered in snow and ice on a beach in Spring Lake, Monmouth County. She still had most of her <u>lanugo</u>. Now she has molted into most of her yearling coat and has learned to swallow fish whole. Her diet consists of about eight pound of fish per day. She still spends most of her day sleeping but is beginning to show excitement when mealtime is close.

A male harbor seal found in Ocracoke, North Carolina, on January 26 suffered from shark bites. He was taken to Brigantine's center so that his wounds would have a chance to heal. He's coming along nicely. According to his chart, "He is very eager at mealtimes, and happily consumes ten pounds of fish daily."

But that was only the beginning. MMSC has rescued 31 seals since the first of the year. Last year's total was about 60. It's very unusual to treat so many by February.

When rescuers first bring an animal to the center, they clean it, give it plenty of water, and then let it rest <u>undisturbed</u>. A veterinarian examines the animal, tests blood, and gives medicine if needed. The animals are cleaned and fed every day. They are left alone as much as possible, with only video cameras to monitor their activities. This helps keep the animals from becoming dependent on humans.

Before releasing them to the ocean, center workers tag all seals. Each tag, attached to a hind flipper, has a number. Tagging gives the center information about where the seals go.

No one is exactly sure why so many seals have come ashore this year. MMSC staff thinks that some seals, such as gray seals, may be overpopulated. This would make it difficult for them to find food in their traditional feeding grounds.

With so many seals washing up, the center wants to remind people what to do if they come across one on a beach. While the mammals may look sweet, they are still wild animals and may bite. It is very important to alert the center right away. Do not try to handle the animal.

16 Study this web.

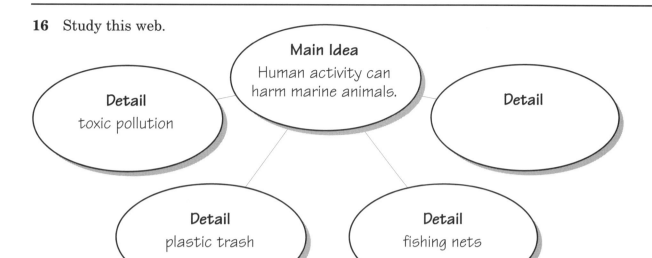

Main Idea
Human activity can harm marine animals.

Detail
toxic pollution

Detail

Detail
plastic trash

Detail
fishing nets

Which of the following best completes the web?

Ⓐ shark bites   Ⓒ large boats

Ⓑ tags   Ⓓ diseases

---

17 This passage is in the form of a(n)—

Ⓐ encyclopedia article.   Ⓒ letter.

Ⓑ book chapter.   Ⓓ news article.

18 The purpose of the first paragraph is to—

Ⓐ introduce the topic of seals washing ashore in large numbers this year.

Ⓑ give details about how animals are treated at the center.

Ⓒ come to a conclusion about why so many seals have washed ashore this year.

Ⓓ explain the dangers that marine animals face.

19 Which clue from the passage helps you understand the meaning of <u>stranded</u>?

Ⓐ *. . . that have washed ashore on New Jersey beaches.*

Ⓑ *These animals range from 5-pound sea turtles to 25-ton humpback whales.*

Ⓒ *Shark bites are common, as well as illness from parasites and disease.*

Ⓓ *The animals eat plastic trash . . .*

20 When animals are left <u>undisturbed</u> at the center, they are—

Ⓐ disturbed again.

Ⓑ disturbed before they wake up.

Ⓒ not disturbed.

Ⓓ disturbed afterwards.

21 Who is most likely to have a different point of view about rescuing marine animals?

Ⓐ a person who works at an aquarium

Ⓑ a person who studies the ocean and its creatures

Ⓒ a marine mammal trainer

Ⓓ a person who sells seal fur for a living

22 What do workers at the rescue center think may have caused so many seals to wash ashore this season?

Ⓐ too many fishing nets

Ⓑ a very cold winter

Ⓒ too many sharks

Ⓓ overpopulation

GO ON

---

23 Imagine you are in charge of an animal rescue center. Would you make a rule that the wild animals should not become too attached to humans? Why or why not? Explain your answer using examples from the passage. (4 points)

_____

_____

_____

_____

_____

_____

_____

_____

_____

_____

_____

_____

_____

_____

_____

_____

_____

_____

_____

_____

_____

Directions: Use the dictionary entry and pronunciation key to answer questions 24 and 25.

lanugo (lə nü´ gō) *n*. The fine, soft hair on the surface of a leaf or fruit or on the skin of a newborn mammal.

Pronunciation Key: pat, cāke, cãre, fär, less, ēqual, tėrm, it, nīce, lot, ōpen, ôrder, oil, out, cup, pu̇t, rüle, child, long, thin, <u>th</u>is, zh measure

ə represents **a** in about, **e** in taken, **i** in pencil, **o** in lemon, **u** in circus

24 The "u" sound in <u>lanugo</u> is the same as the "u" sound in—

Ⓐ cup.   Ⓒ rule.

Ⓑ put.   Ⓓ circus.

25 In this passage, <u>lanugo</u> means—

Ⓐ the fine, soft hair on a seal's food.

Ⓑ the soft surface of a leaf.

Ⓒ the fine, soft hair on the skin of a young seal.

Ⓓ the skin of a mother seal.

Directions: Use the following index from a book about marine animals to answer question 26.

Index

sea cow, 27
sea lion, 29
seal
      Baikal, 32
      bearded, 32
      Caspian, 33
      elephant, 33
      gray, 34
      harbor, 34
      hooded, 35
      leopard, 35
      ribbon, 42
      ringed, 43
      spotted, 43
senses, 16–17
sight, 17–18
skull, 14–15
smell, 12

26 According to the index, Caspian—

Ⓐ is a kind of sea cow.

Ⓑ has a beard.

Ⓒ has a sense of smell.

Ⓓ is a kind of seal.

 GO ON

Directions: Read the passage and answer the questions that follow.

Flo Jo: First Lady of Speed

People at the 1988 Olympic trials in Indianapolis, Indiana, could hardly believe their eyes. Who was the runner moving into position for the qualifying heat for the 100-meter dash?

This stunning woman had long, flowing, dark hair. The other runners wore plain shorts and tank tops. But this woman wore a colorful, one-legged bodysuit that shimmered in the sun. Most surprising of all, the runner had six-inch-long fingernails painted in a rainbow of colors.

Who was this runner with so much individual style? Her name was Florence Griffith Joyner. And she was about to prove that the way she dressed wasn't the only dramatic thing about her.

Making the Team

Florence Griffith was born in California in 1959. She always had a sense of style and individuality. And she loved to run. She even chased jackrabbits near her father's home in the Mojave Desert!

Griffith ran on track teams in both high school and college. Then she won a spot on the 1984 U.S. Olympic team.

The Olympics were held in Los Angeles, California, that year. Griffith won a silver medal in the 200-meter dash. Her time of 22.04 seconds was only 0.01 of a second away from the Olympic <u>record</u>.

A New Name and a New Mission

By the time the 1988 Olympic trials rolled around, Griffith had married track star Al Joyner. She was now known as Florence Griffith Joyner, or "Flo Jo" for short.

Despite the silver medal she won at the 1984 Olympics, most people didn't expect much from her in 1988. She was competing against many other track stars who were more famous. But Griffith Joyner was tired of being second best. She was determined to be number one in her field.

Running with the Wind

On July 16, 1988, at the Olympic trials, Griffith Joyner exploded out of the blocks. It was the qualifying heat in the 100-meter dash. Just a few seconds after the sprinters took off, Griffith Joyner was far ahead of everyone else. She crossed the finish line in just 10.60 seconds. The world record was 10.76 seconds. It seemed unbelievable that Griffith Joyner had beaten that record by such a wide margin.

The judges quickly determined that Griffith Joyner hadn't broken the record after all. The reason was the wind. If the wind is blowing behind the runners, they are able to move faster than usual. According to international rules, a record doesn't count if the wind is blowing more than 4.47 miles per hour.

The judges checked the wind-speed meter alongside the track. They discovered that the wind had been blowing more than 7 miles an hour. The wind had to be the explanation for her extraordinary time, people thought.

Two and a half hours later, Griffith Joyner and the other sprinters lined up for another qualifying heat. By now, the wind had died down and the meter at the edge of the track measured zero. If anyone set a record in this race, it would be official.

When the starting gun went off, Griffith Joyner burst out of the pack and took the lead immediately. She was well ahead of the rest of the runners when she dashed across the finish line. Her time was an astonishing 10.49 seconds—a new world record! And this time no one could credit the wind for Griffith Joyner's speed.

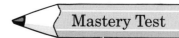

Olympic Gold

The 1988 Olympics began in September. They were held in Seoul, Korea. Everyone was eager to see if Griffith Joyner could repeat her astonishing performance from the trials. She felt confident that she could.

When the starting gun sounded for the quarter finals of the 100-meter dash, Griffith Joyner burst out of the blocks and cruised into the lead. She crossed the finish line 10.62 seconds later, smiling from ear to ear. She was well ahead of everyone else on the track. And her time set a new Olympic record.

Griffith Joyner advanced to the finals, winning the gold medal with a time of 10.54 seconds. But because it was windy, this time wasn't recorded. Still, Griffith Joyner's record remains unbroken.

---

27 The author wrote this passage mostly to—

Ⓒ inform. Ⓒ persuade.

Ⓑ instruct. Ⓓ entertain.

28 Read these statements about the passage. Which one contains bias?

Ⓒ Flo Jo, like all African Americans, was a great athlete.

Ⓑ Flo Jo inspired many young women athletes.

Ⓒ Flo Jo drew large crowds at her competitions.

Ⓓ Flo Jo trained hard for the Olympics.

29 Which of these statements best fits in the section "Making the Team"?

Ⓒ Griffith Joyner also won two other gold medals at the 1988 Olympic Games.

Ⓑ Her high school relay team broke the national record one year.

Ⓒ Griffith Joyner's record remains unbroken.

Ⓓ She was voted Female Athlete of the Year in 1988.

30 Which detail does NOT belong in a brief summary of the passage?

Ⓒ Florence Griffith won a silver medal at the 1984 Olympics.

Ⓑ Griffith Joyner had both speed and a lot of individual style.

Ⓒ The 1988 Olympics began in September.

Ⓓ At the 1988 Olympic trials, Griffith Joyner broke a world record.

31 In the beginning of the section "Running with the Wind" readers may predict that Griffith Joyner can only win with the help of the wind. Which sentence is the first clue that this prediction is not correct?

Ⓒ *Two and a half hours later, Griffith Joyner and the other sprinters lined up for another qualifying heat.*

Ⓑ *By now, the wind had died down and the meter at the edge of the track measured zero.*

Ⓒ *If anyone set a record in this race, it would be official.*

Ⓓ *When the starting gun went off, Griffith Joyner burst out of the pack and took the lead immediately.*

GO ON

32 Based on what you've read in the passage, the author probably believes—

Ⓐ Flo Jo's colorful clothes were not proper.

Ⓑ Flo Jo was an amazing athlete.

Ⓒ Flo Jo performed poorly at the 1984 Olympics.

Ⓓ Flo Jo's record will be broken soon.

Directions: Read the poem and answer the questions that follow.

Shadow March
by Robert Louis Stevenson

All around the house is the jet-black night;
It stares through the window-pane;
It crawls in the corners, hiding from the light,
And it moves with the moving flame.

Now my heart goes a-beating like a drum,
With the breath of Bogie in my hair,
And all round the candle the crooked shadows come,
And go marching along up the stair.

The shadow of the balusters, the shadow of the lamp,
The shadow of the child that goes to bed—
All the wicked shadows coming, tramp, tramp, tramp,
With the black night overhead.

33 The poet compares the night to a(n)—

Ⓐ house.

Ⓒ person staring.

Ⓑ airplane.

Ⓓ drum.

34 Which of the following contains alliteration?

Ⓐ *All around the house is the jet-black night*

Ⓑ *And all round the candle the crooked shadows come*

Ⓒ *And go marching along up the stair*

Ⓓ *The shadow of the child that goes to bed*

35 Which phrase best describes how the author organized this poem?

Ⓐ into one stanza, in which every other line rhymes

Ⓑ into three stanzas, with no rhyming pattern

Ⓒ into three stanzas, with an ABAB rhyming pattern

Ⓓ into four stanzas, with an AABB rhyming pattern

Points Earned/Total = _____/44

Keeping Score

	Points Earned / Total Points	Percent Score
Tryout Test	/44	%
Test Practice 1 Text Features	/7	%
Test Practice 2 Word Recognition	/7	%
Test Practice 3 Reading Strategies	/9	%
Test Practice 4 Vocabulary Skills	/8	%
Test Practice 5 Evaluating What You Read	/9	%
Test Practice 6 Comprehensive Strategies	/8	%
Test Practice 7 Reading Literature	/8	%
Test Practice 8 Literary Elements	/11	%
Test Practice 9 Literary Devices and Structures	/9	%
Mastery Test	/44	%

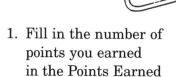

1. Fill in the number of points you earned in the Points Earned box.

2. Use the Finding Percent chart on page 100 to figure out your Percent Score. Then fill in the % box.

3. Compare your Percent Scores for the Tryout Test and the Mastery Test. See how much you've learned!

Finding Percent

Most standardized tests give your score in both number of points earned and in percentages. This handy chart will tell you your percent score.

1. Find the band with the same number of points that are on your test.

2. Follow along the top row of the band to the number of points you earned. Your percent score is right below it.

⇨ Number of Points on Test

7

1	2	3	4	5	6	7
14%	29%	43%	57%	71%	86%	100%

8

1	2	3	4	5	6	7	8
13%	25%	38%	50%	63%	75%	88%	100%

9

1	2	3	4	5	6	7	8	9
11%	22%	33%	44%	56%	67%	78%	89%	100%

11

1	2	3	4	5	6	7	8	9	10	11
9%	18%	27%	36%	45%	55%	64%	73%	82%	91%	100%

44

1	2	3	4	5	6	7	8	9	10	11	12	13	14	15	16	17	18	19	20	21
2%	5%	7%	9%	11%	14%	16%	18%	20%	23%	25%	27%	30%	32%	34%	36%	39%	41%	43%	45%	48%

22	23	24	25	26	27	28	29	30	31	32	33	34	35	36	37	38	39	40	41	42
50%	52%	55%	57%	59%	61%	64%	66%	68%	70%	73%	75%	77%	80%	82%	84%	86%	89%	91%	93%	95%

43	44
98%	100%